Fishes
Freshwater and Marine species

Chatto Nature Guides

British and European
Fishes
Freshwater and
Marine species

Illustrated and identified with colour
photographs

Fritz Terofal

Translated and edited by
Gwynne Vevers

Chatto & Windus · London

Published by
Chatto & Windus Ltd
40 William IV Street
London WC2N 4DF

*

Clarke, Irwin & Co. Ltd
Toronto

British Library Cataloguing in Publication Data
   Terofal, Fritz
      British and European fishes, freshwater and
      marine species.—(Chatto nature guides).
      1. Fishes—Europe—Identification
      I. Title
      597'.09204   QL633
      ISBN 0-7011-2459-8
      ISBN 0-7011-2460-1 Paperback

Title of the original German edition:
Fische

© BLV Verlagsgesellschaft mbH, München, 1978
English Translation © Chatto & Windus Ltd 1979

Printed in Italy

Introduction

This book is intended as a guide to the identification of the fishes living in the fresh waters and seas of north-west Europe and the Mediterranean. The text is illustrated by photographs of living fishes in their natural medium. These photographs have been selected to show the common and most typical species out of the many hundreds that occur in European waters.

Many fish species can be identified quite easily from good photographs, but there are some which require more attention to detail to ensure correct identification. This is where the text should help the observer, as it gives information which cannot be conveyed by pictures. Although the text is written as clearly as possible it does contain some essential ichthyological terms and the following notes should help to explain these. The diagrams on page 6 show the principal external features.

The body of a fish is divided into three regions: the head extending from the tip of the snout to the rear edge of the opercula or gill covers, the trunk extending from the gill covers to the anus, and the tail from the anus to the end of the caudal fin. The term caudal penduncle is given to that part of the body between the end of the anal fin and the insertion of the caudal fin. The total length of a fish is defined as the distance between the tip of the snout and the rear edge of the caudal fin, while the standard length is measured from the tip of the snout to the middle of the end of the caudal peduncle, that is to the last vertebra of the skeleton. Snout length is the distance between the tip of the snout and the front edge of the eye.

It is characteristic of fishes to have fins which are folds of skin supported, in bony fishes, by fin rays. These articulate with the bony pterygiophores of the skeleton and with the help of small muscles they can be folded or extended. There are two

External features of a fish

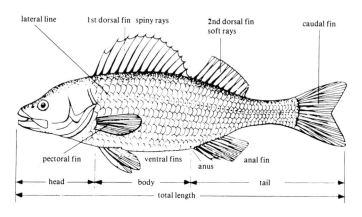

lateral line | 1st dorsal fin spiny rays | 2nd dorsal fin soft rays | caudal fin

pectoral fin | ventral fins | anus | anal fin

head | body | tail

total length

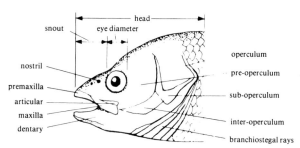

head
snout | eye diameter

nostril
premaxilla
articular
maxilla
dentary

operculum
pre-operculum
sub-operculum
inter-operculum
branchiostegal rays

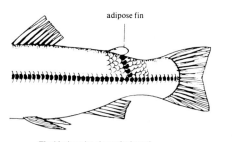

adipose fin

The black scales above the lateral line indicate how the transverse scale series is to be counted.

fish's head with barbels

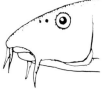

Barbels occur in sturgeons, catfishes, loaches, cod and relatives and some members of the carp and barb family.

6

types of fin ray, namely the unjointed spiny rays which are always pointed at the outer end and usually well ossified, and the jointed soft rays, which may be pointed or branched at the outer end. Soft rays are usually flexible, or occasionally weakly ossified as, for example, the first dorsal fin rays of some carps. When both types of fin ray are present, the spiny rays are always in front of the soft rays. The dorsal fin of the Eelpout forms an exception to this rule.

In some fishes the dorsal fin rays may develop as separate spines (e.g. sticklebacks) or as venomous spines (e.g. in the weevers). The number of rays in each fin is fairly constant for a given species, so this constitutes a valuable character for identification.

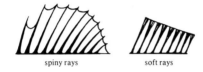

spiny rays   soft rays

The unpaired fins (dorsal, caudal, anal), arranged along the middle line of the fish's body, originally arose as a continuous fold. In the Salmon and some other fishes, including many catfishes, there is a skin fold between the dorsal and caudal fins which is known as the adipose fin; it is not supported by fin rays.

The pectoral fins are paired organs which correspond with the front limbs of terrestrial vertebrates. They are always attached close behind the head. They are developed in various ways according to their function in the different species. In the gurnards, for instance, the three lowermost pectoral fin rays are separate from one another and movable and they serve as sensory organs.

The ventral or pelvic fins are also paired organs and they correspond to the hind limbs of land vertebrates. They too vary in form. In the gobies, suckerfishes and lumpsuckers they are modified to form suckers, while in eels and pipefishes they are completely lacking. When ventral fins are present their position on the body provides a good clue to the identification of certain major groups. They are well behind the pectoral fins in the salmon and carp families, close behind or between the pectorals in the perch family and in front of the pectorals in the cod family.

A fish's body is covered by a transparent, many-layered epidermis in which numerous mucus cells are embedded. The mucus secretions serve to reduce friction when the fish is swimming and also to provide a valuable protection against the ingress of skin parasites and poisonous substances. Beneath the epidermis lies the corium, also with numerous layers of cells, which contains blood and lymph vessels, as well as pigment cells and fat. It is in this layer that the scales are produced. These can be differentiated into cycloid scales which have a smooth rear edge (e.g. in the carp family) and ctenoid scales which have tiny spines on the rear edge (e.g. in the perch family). The roughness of ctenoid scales can be felt if the hand is drawn along a fish's body from tail to head. The scales increase in size as the fish grows and in doing so they produce annual growth rings which are used in determining the age of a fish.

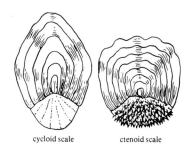

cycloid scale   ctenoid scale

In selachians (sharks and rays) the scales are completely different. Known as placoid scales they are bony structures anchored in the corium, each with a spiny process which projects through the epidermis. In sharks the whole body is covered with these scales, but in rays certain parts of the body are scaleless, and in the Electric Ray scales are completely lacking.

The often very brilliant coloration of fishes is produced by pigment cells or chromatophores, which contains dark brown, yellow or red pigments In many cases the colours become intensified during the breeding period. In certain fishes the juveniles have a special coloration as, for example, the parr stage of Salmon in which the sides of the fish are marked with a number of transverse bars. The silvery iridescence of fishes is due to the reflection of light from crystals of guanine held in cells known as iridocytes.

During the breeding period some species of the carp family develop small, pearl-like tubercles on the epidermis, particularly on the head and the front part of the body.

Fishes have a sensory system known as the lateral line which enables them to perceive objects in the vicinity other than by sight. The lateral line consists of a series of small sensory pits which lie free on the skin (e.g. in the Minnow), in a groove (e.g. in the Pike) or in a mucus-filled canal which communicates with the outside world by short ducts and pores. In many fishes this series of pores can be clearly seen as a thin line running along each side of the body; the lateral line has numerous branches on the head. The course and the number of pierced scales (lateral line scales) provide important clues to

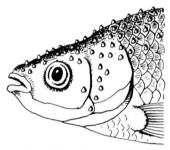

Common Bream showing nuptial tubercles

the identification of species.

The position of the mouth is also characteristic. If the lower jaw is longer than the upper jaw, as in the Asp and the Danube Bleak, the mouth is said to be dorsal, if both jaws are of equal length the mouth is terminal, as in Brown Trout and Common Perch, and if the upper jaw is longer the mouth is ventral.

Many bottom-living fishes, such as sturgeons, catfishes, loaches and some carps and barbs have paired appendages round the mouth known as barbels. These carry taste buds and serve in locating food. Many species of the cod family have a characteristic unpaired, single barbel on the chin. Since

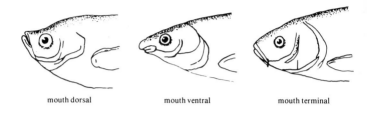

mouth dorsal   mouth ventral   mouth terminal

the number and position of the barbels is characteristic for each species they help in identification.

Some fishes have simple or branched outgrowths of skin above the eyes (e.g. in blennies) or round the nostrils.

Fishes breathe by means of gills which are delicate skin lamellae, richly vascularized, which are supported by cartilaginous gill arches. Water taken in at the mouth passes over the gill lamellae, where the blood takes up dissolved oxygen and releases carbon dioxide. In sharks and rays the gill openings appear externally and are uncovered, but in bony fishes the delicate gills are protected by flat gill covers (opercula). Some of the sharks and all the rays have a special opening behind each eye. These supplementary openings enable the fish to take in water for respiration when it is lying half-buried in the substrate. A few fishes (e.g. loaches) can acquire oxygen by taking water into the alimentary canal where oxygen is absorbed.

On their inner sides, facing the pharynx, the gill arches have spiny processes known as gill-rakers. These structures are particularly long and numerous in fishes that feed on plankton, where they serve to retain the food.

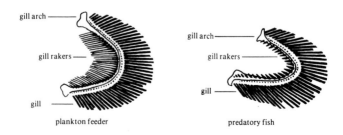

plankton feeder   predatory fish

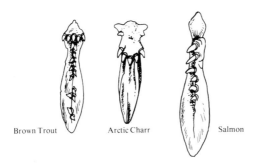

Brown Trout   Arctic Charr   Salmon

The arrangement of the teeth on the jaws and in the mouth cavity also provides useful clues for identification. In sharks and rays teeth are only developed on the jaws, where they lie in several rows, one behind the other, the oldest and longest being at the outer edge of the jaw. As these front teeth become worn they are replaced by those in the next row.

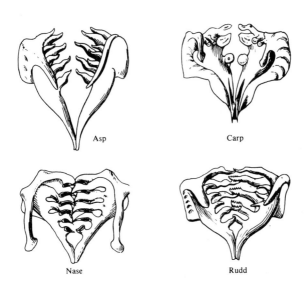

Asp   Carp

Nase   Rudd

The size and form of the teeth is characteristic for each species. In bony fishes, teeth may be developed not only on the jaws, but also in other parts of the mouth. Thus in the salmon family teeth are developed on the vomer, a longish bone in the middle of the palate, and these are important in species identification. The vomer has a broad anterior head and a long posterior shaft. In Brown Trout both parts carry teeth, in the Arctic Charr only the head and in Salmon only the shaft.

Carp and related fishes have no teeth on the jaws, but instead have broad, flat or pointed teeth on the pharyngeal bones in the throat. The old teeth are replaced by new ones, particularly during the autumn and winter months when little or no feeding is taking place. Their number, shape and arrangement is quite characteristic for each species in the carp family, so that they provide a reliable identification character.

Salmon larva   Cod larva

The habits of fishes vary considerably according to the species. Thus, one can differentiate between stationary fishes which never move far from their home range and frequently have a special territory, and migratory fishes which undertake long migrations, usually to reach their breeding grounds. Anadromous species, such as Salmon, migrate from the sea to fresh water for spawning, whereas catadromous species, such as the Common Eel, move from fresh water to the sea. Some fish species spawn in shoals, other in pairs. Eggs and sperm are usually shed into the water at random, while the spawning fishes swim close together, sometimes belly to belly (e.g. in the cod family and in dragonets). In the livebearing bony fishes and in all cartilaginous fishes, copulatory organs are present so that the eggs can be fertilized within the body of the female (sharks, rays, Father Lasher, Norway Haddock). The eggs are usually transparent, greenish, yellowish or reddish, and are either heavier than water so that they sink to the bottom, where they adhere to rocks and plants (in many freshwater fishes spawning over gravel) or they are somewhat lighter so that they float free in the water (flatfishes and the cod family). The number of eggs shed depends upon the age, weight and general condition of the female and on the egg size. Fishes which practise some form of brood protection produce only a small number of egg (e.g. Miller's Thumb, sticklebacks; Bitterling). The period over which the eggs develop depends primarily upon the water temperature, and may vary, according to the species, from a few hours to several months. The newly hatched young, known as larvae, bear only a slight resemblance to their parents.

Sturgeon *Acipenser sturio*

Acipenseridae

Characteristics: body shark-like, with 5 longitudinal rows of large bony plates. Dorsal fin close to the tail, caudal fin with an elongated upper lobe. Snout pointed and half the length of the head. Mouth small, toothless, ventral and protrusible, with a transverse row of 4 barbels which are not frayed. Sides with 20-40 narrow plates, belly with 11-13 ventral plates. Back bluish to greenish-blue, sides shiny silver-grey, belly whitish. Average length 1-2 m, maximum up to 6 m (400 kg). —**Distribution:** north-east Atlantic coastal waters, North and Baltic Seas, Mediterranean and Black Seas. Populations now much reduced.—**Habits:** migratory, moving in April-May from the sea into rivers for breeding. Spawning in June-July over gravelly bottoms. The 800,000-2,400,000 eggs (diameter c. 3 mm) adhere to the gravel, and hatch in 3-6 days. The larvae resemble tadpoles and are c. 10 mm long. After 1-2 years in fresh water the juveniles migrate to the sea. Males are sexually mature at 7-9 years (110-150 cm), females at 8-14 years (120-180 cm).—**Diet:** bottom-living animals (worms, crustaceans, insect larvae, molluscs, small fishes).

Sterlet *Acipenser ruthenus*

Acipenseridae

Characteristics: body shark-like, with a long, narrow, slightly upturned snout and 4 frayed barbels. Sides with 60-70 small, overlapping plates, belly with 10-18 ventral plates. Back grey to brownish with green iridescence, belly yellowish to reddish-white. Average length 35-45 cm, maximum up to 80 cm.—**Distribution:** rivers flowing into the Black and Caspian Seas and the eastern Baltic; also in large lakes in this area.—**Habitat:** lives in deep water during winter.—**Diet:** mainly insect larvae, taken from rocks, submerged timber etc., also worms, small crustaceans and snails. Spawning takes place in May-June, over gravelly ground. The 11,000-140,000 eggs (diameter c. 3 mm) adhere to the gravel and hatch in 4-5 days. Males are sexually mature at 4-5 years (c. 35 cm), females at 5-9 years (40-45 cm).

Salmon   *Salmo salar*   Salmonidae

Characteristics: body spindle-shaped, somewhat laterally compressed with a relatively small, pointed head and a slender caudal peduncle. Adipose fin present. Mouth wide, extending to behind the eyes; old males have a hooked lower jaw. Teeth on the shaft of the vomer, the number decreasing with age. Gill rakers on the 1st gill are all slender. There are 11-15 (usually 12-14) scales (including the lateral line scale) between the adipose fin and the lateral line. Coloration varies according to age class: young fish (opposite, above) up to 15 cm long (parr stage) have large dark markings on the sides, with a red spot between each; larger fish (opposite, centre) moving down to the sea lose the markings on the sides, the back becomes darker and the sides silvery (smolts). Mature adults (opposite, below) ready to spawn show bluish and reddish iridescence, red and black markings, and the male has a reddish belly. Average length 50-120 cm, maximum up to 150 cm.—**Distribution:** both sides of the Atlantic. In European coastal waters from Portugal to the White Sea, also North and Baltic Seas. In many areas the populations are much reduced.—**Habits:** a typical migratory fish which feeds in the sea (fishes, crustaceans) but moves into fresh water for breeding. Migration up the rivers may be in winter or summer, and no food is taken during these periods. Spawning occurs in September-February, in cool, fast-flowing rivers at a depth of 0.5-3 m. By powerful beats of the tail the female makes a spawning pit or redd c. 2-3 m long and 10-30 cm deep. The male and female swim close to one another and with much trembling and snapping of the jaws release the eggs and sperm. The redd closes over as the female digs another one just upstream. Spawning lasts c. 3-14 days, the females laying c. 2,000 eggs (diameter 5-7 mm) for each kg of their weight. The slightly sticky eggs sink to the bottom and lie embedded in the gravel. Most parent fish die after spawning; only 4-6% spawn a second time, c. 1% a third time. After 70-200 days, depending upon the water temperature, the eggs hatch into larvae c. 20 mm long which live for about 6 weeks on the contents of their yolk sac. The young fish remain 1-5 years in fresh water, and when 10-19 cm long they gradually assume the smolt coloration and move downstream. After 1-4 years in the sea they migrate back to spawn in the river where they were hatched.

Brown Trout *Salmo trutta fario*

Salmonidae

Characteristics: body torpedo-shaped, somewhat laterally compressed, with a shortish snout. Adipose fin present. Scales small; between the adipose fin and the lateral line there are 14-19 (usually 16) scales (including the lateral line scale). Mouth wide, extending to behind the eyes; the 2-5 upper gill rakers are blunt. The vomer bone has 2-6 teeth on its head and 9-18, usually in a double row, on the shaft. Coloration varies considerably, depending upon the locality. Back usually greenish to brownish, sides paler, belly whitish to yellowish. Along and below the lateral line there are red markings with pale borders. Adipose fin with a red tip. Young fish (opposite, above) with 6-9 dark transverse markings. Average length 25-40 cm.—**Distribution:** Europe eastwards to the Urals and Asia Minor, in the cool waters, rich in oxygen, of rivers and lakes with gravel bottoms. Introduced into many places outside Europe. The Brown Trout is a non-migratory, relatively small form of the species *S. trutta,* the migratory form being the larger Sea Trout, *S. t. trutta.* Brown Trout, particularly older individuals, take up a territory with hiding-places which they defend against intruders. Juveniles feed on invertebrates, such as small crustaceans and insects including those flying, which they leap for. Large individuals also take tadpoles and small fishes. Spawning takes place in September-February (usually October-January), in running water. The female develops a protruding genital papilla, the male a more intense coloration. By beating her tail the female makes an oval pit or redd about 20-50 cm diameter, in which she lays c. 1,000 orange to reddish eggs (diameter 4-5 mm). After being fertilized by the male they are covered over with gravel. The parents then move back to their territory. The rate of development depends upon the locality, the food supply and the water temperature. Brown Trout become sexually mature at a length of 20-25 cm, the males usually in their 2nd year, the females in their 3rd year.

Lake Trout   *Salmo trutta lacustris*
Salmonidae

Characteristics: body torpedo-shaped, somewhat laterally compressed, older individuals having higher backs than juveniles. Mouth wide, extending to behind the eyes. Vomer bone usually with 4-6 teeth on the head, while the shaft normally has a single row of teeth in front, a double row behind. Back usually blue-green or brownish-green, sides paler with irregular black markings of various sizes, interspersed with brown to reddish dots and circles, particularly in young individuals. Average length 40-80 cm, maximum up to 140 cm.—**Distribution:** in large, deep lakes in the Alps, Scandinavia, Scotland, Wales and Ireland, up to 1,800 m.—**Habits:** older specimens live at depths down to 40 m, whereas the young are found in the upper water layers, often close to the banks. The young feed on invertebrates, the adults on fishes. Spawning occurs in October-December, either in lakes or in rivers feeding them. Females lay 1,000-2,000 eggs (diameter c. 5 mm) for each kg of their weight. The young move back into the lake when 1-2 years old. Males are sexually mature at 3-4 years, females at 4-5 years.

Rainbow Trout   *Salmo gairdneri*
Salmonidae

Characteristics: similar in form to the Brown Trout. Caudal fin always somewhat concave. Sides with a broad, reddish longitudinal band. Head, body, back, adipose fin and caudal fin with small black spots. Average length 25-30 cm, maximum up to 70 cm (c. 7 kg).—**Distribution:** northern America, whence it has been introduced, since 1880, into several other parts of the world.—**Habits:** does not have such high oxygen requirements as the Brown Trout, is less sensitive to high water temperatures, not so dependent upon suitable hiding-places, nor such a fastidious feeder. It is therefore more important as a commercial fish, raised in trout farms. Spawning occurs in December-May. The male makes the spawning pit. The female lays 1,600-2,000 eggs per kg of her body weight. The young grow rapidly and are sexually mature in about their 3rd year.

Arctic Charr   *Salvelinus alpinus salvelinus*
Salmonidae

Characteristics: body slender in the young, more stocky in older individuals. Adipose fin present. Scales very small, 190-240 along the lateral line; 36-37 scales between the adipose fin and the lateral line. Teeth on the head of the vomer. Back grey-green, blue-green or brown, sides paler with pale round spots, belly whitish to yellowish, at spawning time red or orange. Front of the anal and paired fins with a conspicuous white border. Average length 25-40 cm.—**Distribution:** some populations are migratory in the coastal waters and rivers of the Arctic, others live in cold, deep lakes, with water rich in oxygen, throughout the northern hemisphere, including Britain.—**Habits:** the different forms show considerable variation in diet, rate of growth, and time and place of spawning. Most spawn in November-January, on gravelly bottoms, at depths of 20-80 m.

American Brook Trout   *Salvelinus fontinalis*
Salmonidae

Characteristics: body torpedo-shaped, particularly elongated in the young, and with the caudal fin always somewhat concave. Vomer with 8 teeth on its head, more on the shaft. Back and dorsal fin with pale marbling, sides with red and yellow spots, belly yellowish to reddish. Anal and paired fins with black-and-white front edges. Growth varies according to the locality: at 3-5 years they are 30-40 cm long and weigh 0.5-1 kg; rarely over 45 cm long.—**Distribution:** eastern North America in cold streams with fast-flowing water rich in oxygen. Introduced into Europe about 1884.—**Habits:** a non-migratory, predatory fish, feeding in the open water on worms, small crustaceans, molluscs, insects and their larvae; adults also take small fishes. Spawning occurs in October-December, in shallow pits in the gravel where the current is strong. Females lay c. 2,000 eggs (diameter c. 4 mm) per kg body weight. Males are sexually mature at the end of their 2nd, females at the end of their 3rd year.

Huchen   *Hucho hucho*
Salmonidae

Characteristics: body elongated, almost circular in cross section with a long, flat head and a large adipose fin. Mouth wide. Vomer with 4-8 teeth on the head, none on the shaft. Back brownish or greenish-grey, sides paler with a reddish coppery sheen and numerous irregular small black markings, belly whitish. Average length 60-120 cm, maximum up to 150 cm (c. 15 years old).—**Occurence:** only in the valley of the upper and middle Danube, in cool, fast-flowing waters rich in oxygen.—**Habits:** a non-migratory species which feeds on fishes, establishes a territory and defends it against others of its own species. In March-April the female makes a pit in shallow water and lays c. 1,000 eggs (diameter c. 5mm) per kg body weight. At 8-10°C these hatch in c. 35 days. The larvae shelter among the gravel and at first live on the yolk sac contents. Sexually mature after 3-4 years.

Grayling   *Thymallus thymallus*
Thymallidae

Characteristics: body fairly elongated, laterally compressed with a small head, a pointed snout and an adipose fin. Mouth small, extending at most to the front edge of the eye. Upper jaw protruding, teeth small but well developed. Scales small. The long, tall dorsal fin begins far in front of the ventral fins. At spawning time the body shows purple iridescence. Dorsal fin grey, with 4-5 rows of reddish eye-spots. Average length 25-50 cm, maximum up to 60 cm.—**Distribution:** in fast-flowing waters rich in oxygen, over firm ground, in Scandinavia, northern Russia and in scattered areas of Europe, including Britain.—**Habits:** a non-migratory fish, living in shoals, particularly when young.—**Diet:** worms, molluscs, insects, fishes and their eggs. Spawning occurs in March-June, the female beating a pit in a gravel bank, and covering the eggs after fertilization. She lays 3,000-6,000 eggs (diameter 3-4 mm), which hatch in c. 2 weeks. Males are usually sexually mature in their 3rd, females in their 4th year (length c. 30 cm).

Whitefish   *Coregonus* species
Coregonidae

Characteristics: body silvery, somewhat elongated, laterally compressed with a pointed, wedge-shaped head, an adipose fin and a deeply cleft caudal fin. Scales larger than in the Salmonidae. Mouth narrow, extending at most to the front edge of the eye. Teeth small or scarcely developed. Lateral line complete. Due to the large number of different forms and to mixing of populations it is often difficult, or even impossible, to identify the species with any degree of certainty.—**Distribution:** migratory forms in the rivers and coastal waters of the North and Baltic Seas, non-migratory populations in large, deep lakes in the Alps, northern Germany and northern Europe, including Britain.—**Habits:** forms with numerous long gill rakers usually live in open water, feeding on plankton, those with fewer, shorter gill rakers feed mainly on bottom-living animals. Most populations spawn in late autumn and winter, either in open water or near the banks on sandy or gravelly ground.

Smelt   *Osmerus eperlanus*
Osmeridae

Characteristics: body slender, scarcely compressed, translucent, with an adipose fin. Mouth wide, lower jaw protruding, upper jaw extending at least to the rear edge of the eye, dentition powerful. Snout length $1\frac{1}{2}$-$2\frac{1}{2}$ times the eye diameter. scales small, thin, easily detachable. Lateral line ending above the pectoral fins. Back grey-green, sides silvery, with an iridescent longitudinal band at spawning time, belly whitish. Caudal fin with a dark edge. Up to 30 cm long.—**Distribution:** migratory in estuaries and coastal waters from Biscay to southern Norway and in North and Baltic Seas, down to 32 m. Also occurs in large, deep inland lakes, e.g. in the Baltic and Volga areas.—**Habits:** a shoaling fish feeding on planktonic crustaceans, small bottom-living animals and fishes. Spawning occurs in the lower reaches of rivers in March-April, the female producing 9,000-40,000 eggs (diameter 0.6-0.9 mm), which hatch in 2-5 weeks. At a length of 4-5 cm the young move into the sea. Sexually mature at 3-4 years (length 15-18 cm).

Pike *Esox lucius*
Esocidae

Characteristics: body elongated, only slightly laterally compressed, with the anal and dorsal fins positioned far to the rear. Head long with a flat, "duck-bill" snout and a wide mouth, dentition powerful. Back brownish or greenish, sides paler with dark transverse bars, belly whitish to yellowish. Males up to 100 cm long, females up to 150 cm.—**Distribution:** throughout the temperate regions of Europe, Asia and North America, in rivers and lakes.—**Habits:** a non-migratory fish feeding on invertebrates, fishes, amphibians, aquatic birds and small mammals. Spawning occurs in February-May, the female producing 40,000-45,000 eggs (diameter 2.5-3 mm) per kg body weight, which hatch in 10-30 days. Both eggs and larvae adhere to plants etc. The young grow rapidly as soon as they have found a suitable place in which to live. Males are sexually mature at the end of their 2nd, females at the end of their 3rd or 4th year.

Wels *Silurus glanis*
Siluridae

Characteristics: also known as European Catfish. Body scaleless, shiny, with a broad flattened head, a long anal fin, a very short dorsal fin, but no adipose fin. Mouth broad; 2 very long barbels on the upper jaw, 4 shorter ones on the underside of the head. Back blackish-blue, brown or greenish, sides paler with dark marbling, belly off-white with a reddish sheen. Up to 3 m (weight 150 kg).—**Distribution:** central and eastern Europe, introduced elsewhere, including a few places in Britain.—**Habits:** a solitary, nocturnal, bottom-living fish living mainly in warm lakes and large rivers with a soft bottom, and remaining hidden by day.—**Diet:** fishes, frogs, aquatic birds and small mammals. Spawning occurs in May-July, the female laying c. 30,000 eggs (diameter c. 3 mm) per kg body weight, which hatch in 3-10 days. At hatching the larvae are c. 7 mm long and tadpole-like. The male guards them until they have consumed the yolk sac contents, when they leave the nest. Males are sexually mature in 2-3 years, females in 3-4 years.

Roach *Rutilus rutilus*
Cyprinidae

Characteristics: body laterally compressed, with a more or less high back, depending upon age and locality, and with a rounded profile between the ventral fins and the anus. Mouth narrow, almost horizontal. Iris red. Pharyngeal teeth in 1 row. Pectoral, ventral and anal fins reddish. Average length 25-30 cm (7-12 years old), maximum up to 50 cm. —**Distribution:** Europe north of the Pyrenees and Alps eastwards to the Urals, in standing and slow-flowing waters; also in brackish water in the Baltic and Black Seas.—**Habits:** lives usually in shoals among vegetation near the banks, moving to well-protected places in winter.—**Diet:** invertebrates and plants. Spawning occurs in April-May at a water temperature of at least 10°C, when males develop spawning tubercles. A female produces 50,000-100,000 eggs (diameter c. 1 mm), which hatch in 4-10 days. Both eggs and larvae adhere to plants, roots, rocks etc. The fry are free-swimming after 2-5 days. Sexually mature at the end of the 3rd year.

Rudd *Scardinius erythrophthalmus*
Cyprinidae

Characteristics: body laterally compressed, with a somewhat high back and a keeled edge between the ventral fins and the anus. Mouth narrow, sloping steeply upwards. Iris iridescent golden. Pharyngeal teeth in 2 rows. Ventral, anal and caudal fins brownish to grey at the base, otherwise pale red. Average length 20-30 cm, maximum up to 40 cm.—**Distribution:** western, central and eastern Europe in standing and slow-flowing waters; common in England.—**Habits:** living in shoals close to the water surface, often among vegetation near the banks.—**Diet:** aquatic plants and invertebrates. Spawning occurs in April-June, the females laying 90,000-200,000 eggs (diameter c. 1.5 mm), which hatch in 3-10 days into larvae that adhere to plants. After they have consumed the yolk sac contents the larvae feed at first on animal plankton. Sexually mature at the end of the 2nd or 3rd year. Rudd hybridize with Roach, Silver Bream and Bleak.

Dace   *Leuciscus leuciscus*
Cyprinidae

Characteristics: body spindle-shaped. Mouth narrow, caudal fin edge concave, pharyngeal teeth in 2 rows. Back bluish-green, sides yellowish to silvery, belly whitish. Pectoral, ventral and anal fins yellowish to orange. Average length 15-20 cm, maximum up to 30 cm.—**Distribution:** Europe north of the Pyrenees and Alps, except Scotland, western and northern Norway, western and southern Balkans. Mainly living in fast-flowing waters with sandy or gravelly bottoms.—**Habits:** a gregarious surface-living fish and one of the best swimmers among the Cyprinidae.—**Diet:** insects, worms, small snails, and a small amount of plant material. Spawning occurs in March-May, when males have small, white tubercles on the head and body. The eggs (diameter c. 2 mm) sink to the bottom and adhere to water plants and stones. In their first summer the young reach a length of c. 6-7 cm, in the 2nd up to c. 9-11 cm. Sexually mature at the end of the 2nd (rarely) or 3rd year.

Chub   *Leuciscus cephalus*
Cyprinidae

Characteristics: body spindle-shaped, with a broad head. Mouth wide, caudal fin edge convex, pharyngeal teeth in 2 rows. Scales large and coarse, with dark edges. Lateral line with 44-46 scales. Back grey-brown with a greenish sheen, sides silvery, often with a golden sheen, belly whitish. Ventral and anal fins red. Average length 30-50 cm (7-10 years old), maximum up to 60 cm.—**Distribution:** throughout Europe, in rivers, more rarely in lakes.—**Habits:** a surface fish, gregarious when young, but becoming solitary with age. Young individuals feed mainly on worms, small crustaceans, insects and their larvae, molluscs and sometimes plants, adults on other fishes, frogs, freshly moulted crustaceans and even small mammals. Spawning occurs in April-June, when males develop white tubercles. A female lays c. 45,000 eggs (diameter c. 1.5 mm) per kg body weight, which adhere to plants or stones and hatch in c. 1 week. Males are usually sexually mature at 3, females at 4 years.

Ide or Orfe   *Leuciscus idus*
Cyprinidae

Characteristics: body elongated, somewhat high-backed, laterally compressed. Distinguished from the similar Chub by the narrower mouth, smaller scales (55-61 lateral line scales) and concave caudal fin. Back green and blackish-grey, sides usually very silvery, belly whitish (there is also a common yellowish form known as the Golden Orfe). Iris yellow. Ventral and anal fins reddish. Average length 30-40 cm (6-9 years), maximum up to 60 cm.—**Distribution:** Europe north of the Alps from the Rhine to the Urals. Absent from western and southern Europe, except when introduced, e.g. in Britain.—**Habits:** a gregarious, surface-living fish, feeding when young on plankton, and later on worms, small crustaceans, insect larvae and molluscs. Adults also take small fishes. Spawning April-June, in sandy or gravelly places near the banks. Males develop nuptial tubercles. The female produces 40,000-115,000 eggs (diameter 1.5 mm) which adhere to plants and stones, and hatch in 10-20 days. Sexually mature at 3-4 years.

Stroemer   *Leuciscus souffia agassizi*
Cyprinidae

Characteristics: body elongated, almost spindle-shaped, slightly laterally compressed. Mouth terminal. Pharyngeal teeth in 2 rows. Back blackish-grey with a bluish metallic sheen, sides silvery, belly silvery-white, lateral line and the bases of the fins orange. At spawning time there are dark, iridescent violet, longitudinal bands, particularly in the males. Average length 12-17 cm, maximum up to 25 cm.—**Distribution:** three geographical races viz. *L. s. souffia* from the Rhone and Var valleys (French Souffie), *L. s. muticellus,* northern and central Italy and *L. s. agassizi,* upper reaches of the Rhine and Danube.—**Habits:** lives over gravel in running water, more rarely in lakes.—**Diet:** mainly planktonic animals, also worms and other bottom-living animals. Spawning in March-April. A little known cyprinid.

Minnow *Phoxinus phoxinus*
Cyprinidae

Characteristics: body elongated, almost cylindrical, with only the caudal peduncle laterally compressed. Mouth terminal, scales small, lateral line often incomplete. Back usually brownish-green, sides pale, silvery, belly whitish. At spawning time males are darker, with reddish underparts and a pale spot on the gill cover, dark cross bands from the back to below the middle of the sides and an iridescent golden longitudinal stripe. Average length 7-10 cm, maximum up to 14 cm, the females somewhat larger than the males.—**Distribution:** Europe (except southern Spain, southern Italy, Iceland), also northern Asia, mainly in clear rivers and lakes, rich in oxygen.—**Habits:** an adaptable shoaling fish, often living in large numbers close to the surface.—**Diet:** invertebrates on the bottom and in open water, also flying insects. Spawning occurs in April-July, when both sexes develop nuptial tubercles. The female lays 200-1,000 eggs (diameter 1-1.3 mm) where adhere to stones, rarely to plants, and hatch in 5-10 days. Sexually mature at the end of 1-2 years.

Gudgeon *Gobio gobio*
Cyprinidae

Characteristics: body spindle-shaped, with a ventral mouth. Head, eyes and scales relatively large. Mouth with one short barbel at each corner. Back blackish, greenish or bluish-brown, sides paler, with a row of large indistinct markings, belly shiny white. Unpaired fins with small, dark dots. Average length 8-14 cm, maximum up to 20 cm.—**Distribution:** western, central and eastern Europe, mainly in fast-flowing waters with sand or gravel bottoms, but also in lakes.—**Habits:** a gregarious bottom-living fish, living in shallow water during summer, in deeper places in winter.—**Diet:** worms, crustaceans, insect larvae, occasionally also fish eggs. Spawning occurs in May-June, when the male has nuptial tubercles on the head and front of the body. The female lays 1,000-3,000 eggs (diameter 1.5 mm) on stones or plants in shallow running water. These hatch in 10-30 days.

Asp *Aspius aspius*
Cyprinidae

Characteristics: body elongated, somewhat laterally compressed. Mouth wide, lower jaw protruding, eyes and scales relatively small, lateral line with 65-73 scales, caudal fin edge concave. Pharyngeal teeth in 2 rows. Back dark olive-green, with a bluish sheen, sides paler with a golden sheen, belly silvery-white. Paired fins and anal fin reddish. Average length 50-55 cm (4-5 years), maximum up to 100 cm (9 kg).—**Distribution:** Europe north of the Alps from the Elbe and Danube eastwards to the Urals and Caspian Sea, in rivers and large lakes.—**Habits:** a shy, predatory fish living close below the surface, and avoiding waters near the bank. Gregarious when young, feeding then on invertebrates, but becoming more solitary with age when it hunts Dace, Roach and Bleak, and even frogs, mice and small aquatic birds. Spawning occurs in April-June, when the male develops nuptial tubercles. A 2-3 kg female lays 80,000-1,000,000 eggs which adhere to gravel and hatch in 10-17 days (at 8.5-12.5°C). Sexually mature in 4-5 years.

Nase *Chondrostoma nasus*
Cyprinidae

Characteristics: body elongated, slightly laterally compressed, with a protruding snout. Mouth ventral and transverse, lower lip horny with a sharp edge, lateral line with 57-62 scales. Pharyngeal teeth in 1 row. Back grey-blue to grey-green, sides silvery, belly white to yellowish-white. Pectoral, ventral and anal fins yellowish-red to violet. Average length 25-40 cm, maximum up to 50 cm (1.5 kg).—**Distribution:** rivers of north-east France, Rhine and Danube eastwards to the Caspian Sea.—**Habits:** a shoaling fish living near the bottom, usually over gravel banks.—**Diet:** primarily algae, rasped from rocks and roots, and invertebrates living amongst the algae. In winter dense shoals move into deeper water. Spawning occurs in March-May, when both sexes develop spawning tubercles, and migrate upstream to shallow, gravelly areas. The female produces up to 100,000 eggs (diameter 1.5 mm). Sexually mature in 2-4 years.

Tench   *Tinca tinca*
Cyprinidae

Characteristics: body squat, with a tall caudal peduncle and small scales deeply embedded in the thick, slimy skin. Mouth small, terminal, with 1 barbel at each corner, pharyngeal teeth in 1 row, lateral line with 95-100 scales. All fins rounded, the caudal only slightly concave. From the age of 2 years (length c. 12 cm) males can be distinguished by their elongated ventral fins, in which the 2nd ray is thickened. Back usually dark green or dark brown, sides paler with a golden sheen, belly yellowish-white. Average length 20-30 cm, maximum up to 60 cm (7.5 kg).—**Distribution:** throughout Europe, including parts of Britain (not in Dalmatia, Iceland, northern Scotland and northern Scandinavia), living in slow-flowing rivers and shallow, warm lakes with dense vegetation and muddy bottom.—**Habits:** by day mostly hidden near the bottom, coming out at twilight to hunt for food, which consists of small bottom-living invertebrates (worms, insect larvae, small molluscs). During the cold part of the year they stop feeding, bury themselves in the mud and hibernate. Spawning takes place in May-July, depending upon the temperature, but usually at 19-20°C. A 500 g female lays c. 300,000 eggs, the maximum being c. 900,000. The eggs are laid in instalments at intervals of c. 2 weeks and the whole process may take 1½-2 months. The very small eggs (diameter 0.8-1 mm) adhere to water plants. At the temperatue of 20°C they hatch in about 3 days. The newly hatched larvae (length 4-5 mm) have attachment organs on the head which enable them to adhere to plants and thus avoid sinking into the mud. As soon as the gills are functional these organs atrophy. The young feed at first on planktonic animals, but quite soon they change to feeding at the bottom. Tench grow slowly, and are not sexually mature until their 3rd-4th year.

Golden Tench, a reddish-yellow colour variant (opposite, below) is much kept as an ornamental fish in outside ponds and in aquaria, in the same way as the golden forms of the Carp, Ide (Golden Orfe) and, of course, the Goldfish.

Barbel   *Barbus barbus*

Cyprinidae

Characteristics: body elongated, slender with a longish snout and 4 barbels on the edge of the upper lip. Belly profile almost straight, back scarcely curved, mouth ventral. Lips thick, fleshy, pharyngeal teeth in 3 rows. Scales medium-sized, 55-65 in the lateral line. Dorsal and anal fins short, the longest dorsal fin ray strongly serrated at the rear edge. Back usually brown to grey-green, sides paler with a golden sheen, belly whitish often with a reddish sheen. All the fins are greenish-grey, the pectorals, ventrals and anal and the lower lobe of the caudal with a reddish tinge. As in related species there are golden varieties. Average length 30-50 cm, maximum up to 90 cm (8.5 kg).—**Distribution:** parts of England, France eastwards to the Black Sea area, but not in Scotland, Ireland, Denmark or Scandinavia, living on sandy or gravel bottoms of clear rivers rich in oxygen.—**Habits:** a gregarious fish which remains hidden on the bottom by day and usually becomes active at twilight. It feeds mainly at night on small bottom-living invertebrates (worms, insect larvae, molluscs), and fish eggs; older individuals also eat small fishes. During the cold part of the year they congregate in groups in deeper water. Spawning takes place in May-July, when the male develops pearly-white nuptial tubercles on the head and back. The spawning fish gather in large shoals and move upstream to spawn in shallow areas with a strong current. Some 3,000-9,000 yellow eggs (diameter c. 2 mm) are laid and these at first adhere to stones. After a short time they become detached and complete their development hidden among the gravel. They hatch in 10-15 days and the larvae have a resting stage during which they consume their yolk sac contents; they then start to feed on small bottom-living invertebrates, and later move downstream to take up a territory. They become sexually mature at the end of their 3rd or 4th year, when about 25 cm long.

Bleak   *Alburnus alburnus*

Cyprinidae

Characteristics: body slender, elongated, laterally compressed. Mouth facing upwards, lower jaw protruding, not thickened, pharyngeal teeth in 2 rows. Anal fin considerably longer than dorsal fin. Lateral line with 46-53 scales. Keel between ventral fins and anus not scaled. Back greenish-grey to greenish-blue, sides and belly very silvery. Average length 12-15 cm, maximum up to 25 cm.—**Distribution:** in standing and slow-flowing waters north of the Pyrenees and Alps to the Urals. Absent from Scotland and Ireland.—**Habits:** a gregarious surface-living fish which prefers quiet waters and avoids strong currents, cloudy water and very dense vegetation.—**Diet:** planktonic animals, worms, insect larvae. Spawning takes place in shallow water in April-June, when the males develop spawning tubercles. The female produces c. 1,500 sticky eggs which adhere to stones and plants and hatch in c. 1 week. Sexually mature at 2-3 years.

Danube Bleak   *Chalcalburnus chalcoides mento*

Cyprinidae

Characteristics: body slender, elongated, laterally compressed. Mouth facing upwards, lower jaw protruding and thickened, pharyngeal teeth in 2 rows. Anal fin longer than dorsal fin; unlike Bleak the anal fin starts behind the rear end of the dorsal fin. Lateral line with 59-67 scales. Keel between ventral fins and anus not scaled. Back blue-green to blackish-green, sides and belly silvery-white. Maximum length up to c. 40 cm.—**Distribution:** Danube area and a few other rivers flowing into the Black Sea.—**Habits:** a shoaling fish which feeds mainly on planktonic animals, insect larvae and insects that land on the water, more rarely on small bottom-living invertebrates. During the spawning period in April-June the male has nuptial tubercles on the head and front of the body. Spawning takes place in shallow, gravelly areas when some 15,000-23,000 eggs are laid.

Schneider   *Alburnoides bipunctatus*

Cyprinidae

Characteristics: body somewhat high-backed, more squat than in Bleak. Mouth terminal, almost horizontal, pharyngeal teeth in 2 rows. Anal fin longer than dorsal fin. Lateral line complete, curved downwards. Back blue-green to olive-brown, sides paler, belly silvery-white. A dark longitudinal stripe above the lateral line from the gill cover to the caudal peduncle is particularly evident at spawning time. Average length 9-13 cm, maximum up to 16 cm.—**Distribution:** north of the Pyrenees and Alps from France to the Urals (but not in Britain), in clear, fast-flowing waters, up to altitudes of 700 m.—**Habits:** an active shoaling fish, living mostly near the bottom and feeding on plankton and insects. Spawning takes place in May-June over gravelly ground, in a current.

Danube Bream   *Abramis sapa*

Cyprinidae

Characteristics: body much compressed laterally, with a stumpy, arched snout. Mouth slightly ventral, eyes large. Anal fin very long, much longer than in Common Bream, with 41-48 rays. Lower lobe of caudal fin elongated. Lateral line with 41-48 scales. Pharyngeal teeth in 1 row. Back greenish-grey, sides pale whitish-grey with a slight mother-of-pearl sheen, belly whitish. average length 15-20 cm, maximum up to 30 cm.—**Distribution:** from the Danube and its tributaries to the Urals.—**Habits:** a gregarious fish living close to the bottom in large rivers.—**Diet:** worms, small crustaceans, insect larvae and small molluscs, more rarely plants. The fish move upstream for spawning in April-May, when the males develop spawning tubercles. The female lays about 100,000 eggs (diameter c. 2 mm) among vegetation in shallow places near the river banks.

Common Bream *Abramis brama*

Cyprinidae

Characteristics: body high-backed, strongly compressed laterally, with a short dorsal fin and an anal twice as long (26-31 rays). Eye diameter less than snout length. Lateral line with 50-57 scales. Pharyngeal teeth in 1 row. Back lead-coloured to blackish, usually with a greenish sheen, sides paler and iridescent, belly whitish. Older individuals usually with a golden sheen. Unpaired fins dark grey, paired fins pale grey. Average length 30-50 cm, maximum up to 75 cm.—**Distribution:** north of the Pyrenees and Alps from the Atlantic to the Urals, in large lakes and slow-flowing rivers; also in brackish waters in southern Russia and the Baltic area.—**Habits:** the young live in small shoals near the banks, adults in deeper water coming inshore at night to feed on worms, insect larvae and small molluscs. Spawning occurs in May-July in shallow places near the banks. The female lays c. 300,000 yellowish eggs (diameter c. 1.5 mm) which hatch in 3-12 days. The larvae (c. 4 mm long) attach themselves to plants until they have consumed the yolk sac contents. Sexually mature at 3-4 years (length 20-30 cm).

Silver Bream *Blicca bjoerkna*

Cyprinidae

Characteristics: body shape similar to Common Bream. Anal fin with 22-26 rays. Eye diameter greater than or equal to the snout length. Lateral line with 44-50 scales. Pharyngeal teeth in 2 rows. Back greyish-green to blackish-green, sides paler with a silvery sheen, belly whitish to reddish, very silvery. Fins dark grey, the pectorals and ventrals reddish at the base. Average length 20-30 cm, maximum c. 35 cm.—**Distribution:** north of the Pyrenees and Alps, in warm, shallow, low-lying lakes with dense vegetation and in large, slow-flowing rivers.—**Habits:** lives close to the bottom among marginal vegetation and feeds on small invertebrates, plants and planktonic crustaceans. Spawning takes place in May-June in shallow inshore areas, mainly at night. The female lays c. 100,000 pale yellow eggs (diameter c. 2 mm) which adhere to plants. Sexually mature at 3-5 years.

Bitterling *Rhodeus sericeus amarus*

Cyprinidae

Characteristics: body high-backed, laterally compressed with large scales. Mouth small, terminal. Lateral line short, with only 5-6 scales. Pharyngeal teeth in 1 row. Back grey-green to blackish, sides paler, silvery, with an iridescent blue-green longitudinal band running from the middle of the side to the caudal fin, belly whitish, often with a rosy sheen. In males at spawning time (opposite, below) the throat, breast and front of the belly are red, while females have an ovipositor several cm long (opposite, above). Average body length 5-6 cm (2-3 years old), maximum c. 9 cm.—**Distribution:** Europe north of the Pyrenees and Alps (except Britain, Ireland, Denmark, Scandinavia), from France to the Volga and in northern Asia Minor; two other subspecies further east.—**Habits:** a gregarious fish, feeding mainly on aquatic plants and also on invertebrates such as worms, small crustaceans, insect larvae. Spawning takes place in April-June. The male selects a territory containing a Swan Mussel which he defends against other males. At its rear end the bivalve has 2 apertures; water for respiration and food are sucked into the lower, inhalant siphon, while the used water and faeces are expelled at the upper, exhalant siphon. The female positions herself head downwards above the bivalve and watches it. As soon as it opens its shell she very rapidly inserts her ovipositor and lays 1-2 eggs in the mollusc's gill chamber. Simultaneously the male sheds sperm over the mollusc and these are sucked into the inhalant siphon to fertilize the eggs. This process may be repeated several times by the same pair or the female may seek a fresh mate. The female lays a total of 40-100 eggs (diameter 3 mm) which hatch in 2-3 weeks. The larvae have horny outgrowths on the yolk sac with which they adhere to the gills of the Swan Mussel. When the yolk sac contents have been partially consumed the larvae leave the gill chamber and are passed out through the exhalant siphon into the open water.

Bitterling have been introduced into lakes in north-western England.

Crucian Carp   *Carassius carassius*

Cyprinidae

Characteristics: body high-backed, stocky, somewhat laterally compressed with a long, high dorsal fin and a slightly concave caudal fin. Corners of mouth without barbels. Lateral line with 30-35 scales. Pharyngeal teeth in 1 row. Coloration brown to yellowish-brown, back darker with greenish iridescence, belly yellowish to whitish. Caudal peduncle with a dark marking. Pectoral, ventral and anal fins with a reddish sheen. Average length c. 15 cm, maximum c. 45 cm (2-3 kg).—**Distribution:** western, central and eastern Europe in waters that are not too cold nor too fast-flowing. Prefers shallow ponds and lakes with dense vegetation.—**Habits:** a very adaptable fish which even tolerates a certain amount of pollution and oxygen deficiency. During the winter Crucian Carp dig into the bottom and undergo a kind of hibernation. They feed on plants and small bottom-living invertebrates, particularly mayfly and mosquito larvae. For spawning they congregate in May-June in shallow areas with dense vegetation. The pale orange eggs (diameter 1-1.5 mm) are laid and fertilized at a temperature of above 14°C (optimum 19-20°C). The female produces 150,000-300,000 eggs which hatch in 3-7 days. The newly hatched larvae (length 4.2-4.9 mm) have attachment organs in front of the eyes, with which they adhere to water plants until they have consumed the contents of the yolk sac. As soon as they can swim they start to feed on tiny planktonic animals. The young grow very fast when conditions are favourable. Sexual maturity is reached at an age of 3-4 years when they are 8-15 cm long; after the 2nd year the females grow faster than the males, but the latter are the first to become sexually mature. Special fast-growing races have been bred which become sexually mature at the end of the 2nd year, at a length of 13-15 cm. These are farmed in certain places, particularly in eastern Europe.

Like many other species the Crucian Carp produces yellowish-red colour variants. The golden form (opposite, below) is, however, not very suitable for stocking ornamental ponds because, being a bottom-living fish, it rarely comes to the surface and is hardly ever seen.

Prussian Carp   *Carassius auratus gibelio*
Cyprinidae

Characteristics: similar in shape to the Crucian Carp, and without barbels. Lateral line with 28-32 scales. Pharyngeal teeth in 1 row. Paler and more silvery-yellow than the Crucian Carp, and lacking the black marking on the caudal peduncle. Maximum length c. 45 cm (c. 3 kg).—**Distribution:** originally from the Amur basin in eastern Asia, this fish has been widely distributed by man. In Europe it now occurs in standing and slow-flowing waters with dense vegetation and soft bottoms.—**Habits:** an omnivorous fish which grows somewhat faster than the Crucian Carp and is therefore farmed as a pond fish, particularly in eastern Europe. Sexually mature at the end of the 3rd or 4th year (15-20 cm length) or with supplementary feeding at the end of the 2nd year. In populations lacking males, the females join in the spawning shoals of related species (Carp, Crucian Carp) whose sperm stimulates cell division in Prussian Carp eggs. These unfertilized eggs produce only females.

Goldfish   *Carassius auratus auratus*
Cyprinidae

Characteristics: the wild form is similar in shape to the Prussian Carp with somewhat larger scales. Lateral line with 26-31 scales. Careful selection over a long period in China and Japan has produced numerous variants (veiltail, comet, lion head etc.).—**Distribution:** the original range extended from eastern Europe to China. Ornamental Goldfish started to arrive in Europe in the 17th century. Nowadays they occur wild in ponds and slow-flowing rivers in Italy, southern France and Portugal, where they breed successfully. On account of their conspicuous coloration they do not, of course, do well in waters with a large stock of predatory fishes. They are very commonly kept in aquaria and ponds.—**Habits:** spawning takes place in April-May at a temperature of 18-22°C and the eggs hatch in 5-7 days. The almost transparent larvae attach themselves by adhesive organs on the head to aquatic plants. Like the original wild form the young are at first grey or olive-green, and only become golden (or silver) after several months.

Carp *Cyprinus carpio*

Cyprinidae

Characteristics: the original form (scaled carp, opposite, above) has an elongated, somewhat laterally compressed body and a protrusible terminal mouth with 4 barbels on the upper lip. Lateral line with 33-40 scales, pharyngeal teeth in 3 rows. Back usually brownish-green to blackish-green, sides silvery-brown, belly whitish. Fins grey-green, the paired and anal fins often with a reddish tinge. Maximum length up to c. 120 cm (25-30 kg, age 40 years). Three forms with either an elongated or a high-backed body can be distinguished on the basis of their scales: 1. scaled carp with a complete covering of scales; 2. mirror carp (opposite, below) with mirror-like scales distributed irregularly, or linearly along the lateral line; 3. leather carp with no scales or only a few.—**Distribution:** originally Asia from the Black Sea to Manchuria. Introduced almost everywhere in Europe as a pond fish, later to North America, Australia and elsewhere. Prefers warm standing or slow-flowing waters with a sandy or muddy bottom and dense vegetation.—**Habits:** usually spends the day in deep, sheltered places, under overhanging trees or among aquatic vegetation, and becomes active at twilight. Carp feed on invertebrates (worms, small crustaceans, insect larvae, small molluscs) and plants. Large individuals also take small fishes and newts. Breeding takes place in May-July. The male has fine white nuptial tubercles on the head and front of the body. Spawning occurs in instalments at intervals of a week, in quiet, shallow water with plants, and close to the banks. The female produces 200,000-300,000 eggs per kg weight. The glass-clear eggs (c. 1 mm diameter swelling to c. 1.6 mm in water) adhere to plants and hatch in 3-5 days. The newly hatched larvae (c. 5 mm long) hang by the adhesive head organ from plants for a further 1-5 days. They must then try to reach the surface to fill the swimbladder with air. As soon as they can swim they feed on plant and animal plankton (algae, rotifers, small crustaceans) and from a length of c. 18 mm start to search for bottom-living invertebrates. Growth depends upon temperature and food supply. Males are usually sexually mature at the end of their 3rd year, females at the end of their 3rd or 4th year.

Spined Loach   *Cobitis taenia*
Cobitidae

Characteristics: head and body laterally compressed, with very small, thin scales and 6 short barbels. Lateral line incomplete. A movable double spine below each eye. In males the 2nd pectoral fin ray is thickened. Back and sides off-white, the back with dark marbling, the sides with a longitudinal row of large dark markings. Dorsal and caudal fins with rows of dark dots. Average length 5-10 cm, maximum c. 12 cm. Males smaller than females.—**Distribution:** throughout Europe in clear rivers and lakes with a sandy or muddy bottom.—**Habits:** buries itself by day, leaving only the head exposed, and becomes active at night.—**Diet:** invertebrates such as rotifers and small crustaceans. The sticky eggs, laid in April-June, adhere to rocks and roots, and there is no brood protection. This species is very sensitive to the quality of the water and in some places its populations have been much reduced by pollution.

Stone Loach   *Noemacheilus barbatulus*
Cobitidae

Characteristics: body cylindrical, only the caudal peduncle being laterally compressed. No spines below eyes. Lateral line pale and clearly discernible. Caudal fin edge straight, only slightly indented. Upper jaw with 6 barbels. Back and sides grey to brown with darker markings, belly whitish. Dorsal and caudal fins with rows of dark spots. Average length 8-12 cm (at 2-3 years), maximum c. 16 cm.—**Distribution:** west, central and east Europe, in shallow, fast-flowing rivers over a gravelly bottom and near the banks in clear lakes.—**Habits:** a bottom-living, non-migratory fish, which is usually hidden under rocks by day.—**Diet:** small crustaceans, insect larvae (e.g. mayfly), fish eggs. Spawning occurs in April-May, when both sexes have spawning tubercles on the insides of the pectoral fins. The eggs (c. 1 mm diameter) adhere to stones and are guarded by the male until they hatch. They become sexually mature in their 2nd or 3rd year.

Eel *Anguilla anguilla*

Anguillidae

Characteristics: body snake-like with a slimy skin in which the tiny, longish-oval scales are deeply embedded. The dorsal, caudal and anal fins are continuous. Ventral fins absent. Yellow eels have the back olive-brown or grey-brown, and the belly silvery-yellow. Silver eels have a dark grey-green back and very silvery sides and belly. Males up to 51 cm, females up to 150 cm (6 kg).—**Distribution:** Europe (Canaries and Azores to Iceland and White Sea), west coasts of Africa, Mediterranean, North and Baltic Seas, in rivers and lakes with access to the sea.—**Habits:** a bottom-living fish active at twilight. Yellow eels feed in fresh water on worms, small crustaceans, insect larvae, small molluscs, small fishes, frogs. After 4-10 years they migrate downstream to the sea as silver eels and cross the Atlantic to spawn in an area close to the Sargasso Sea.

Burbot *Lota lota*

Gadidae

Characteristics: body elongated with a broad, flat head and a wide, slightly ventral mouth. Scales small, delicate. One long barbel on the chin, 1 very short one at each nostril. First dorsal fin short, 2nd dorsal and anal fins very long. Ventral fins on the throat. Caudal fin rounded. Coloration yellowish-olive or greenish, with darker marbling, sides paler, belly whitish. Average length 30-60 cm, maximum c. 100 cm.—**Distribution:** Europe and Asia, but scarce in Britain.—**Habits:** the only freshwater member of the cod family. Active at twilight and during the night, feeding when young on worms, small crustaceans, insect larvae and molluscs, when adult on fish eggs and fry. In November-March, at a temperature of 0.5-4°C, the female produces c. 500,000 eggs (diameter c. 1 mm) per kg weight; these have an oil globule and float in the water. They hatch in 1½-2½ months, and the larvae float near the surface. Males are sexually mature at the end of their 3rd, females at the end of their 4th year.

Perch *Perca fluviatilis*
Percidae

Characteristics: body more or less high-backed with small scales. First dorsal fin with 13-17 spiny rays and a black mark at the rear end. Gill cover with a strong spine. Back dark grey to bluish or olive-green, sides with 6-9 dark transverse markings, belly paler. Ventral and anal fins reddish. Males more brightly coloured. Average length 15-30 cm, maximum c. 45 cm.—**Distribution:** Europe, except northern Norway, northern Scotland, Spain, Portugal, central and southern Italy, western Balkans, in running and standing waters.—**Habits:** a non-migratory fish preferring clear water and a hard bottom, but without a strong current. Living in shoals when young, often solitary when adult and feeding mainly on young fishes. Spawning is in March-June at 7-8°C. The eggs (diameter 1.5-2 mm) are laid in gelatinous threads on water plants or rocks in shallow water. They hatch in 2-3 weeks. Males become sexually mature at the end of their 2nd year (9-10 cm) at the earlist, females usually at the end of their 3rd-4th year.

Zander *Stizostedion lucioperca*
Percidae

Characteristics: body pike-shaped, with a wide mouth. Jaws with large fangs and numerous small teeth. Two separated dorsal fins. Back and sides greenish to grey, belly whitish. Dorsal fin with rows of dark dots, caudal fin with small dark markings. Juveniles have 8-10 dark transverse bars on the upper half of the body. Average length 40-50 cm, maximum up to 120-130 cm (12-15 kg).—**Distribution:** central and eastern Europe, introduced elsewhere. Prefers warm waters and a hard bottom.—**Habits:** a predatory fish of the open waters, avoiding dense marginal vegetation.—**Diet:** small fishes. Spawns in April-May at a temperature of 12-15°C. The female lays 150,000 to 200,000 eggs per kg weight and these adhere to roots and submerged branches. The eggs (diameter 1-1.5 mm) are guarded by the male and hatch in c. 1 week into larvae 5-6 mm long. Males become sexually mature in 2-4 years (33-37 cm), females in 3-5 years (40-44 cm).

Ruffe *Gymnocephalus cernua*
Percidae

Characteristics: body squat with a shortish head which has conspicuous sensory canals particularly at the front of the gill cover and below the eye. Dorsal fin undivided. Gill cover with a long spine. Back olive-green to grey-green with dark markings, breast somewhat reddish, belly whitish. Dorsal and caudal fins with rows of dark markings. Average length 12-15 cm, maximum up to 25 cm.—**Distribution:** Europe north of the Pyrenees and Alps, except Ireland, Scotland, western and northern Norway and parts of the Balkans, in large rivers and lakes.—**Habits:** lives gregariously in deepish waters with a sandy bottom, and is relatively resistant to water pollution.—**Diet:** worms, crustaceans, molluscs, insect larvae and fish eggs. Spawns in March-May, at a temperature of 10-15°C, when the shoals move into shallow water. The female lays 50,000-100,000 yellowish-white eggs (diameter 0.5-1 mm) on rocks and plants; they hatch in 8-12 days. The fish are sexually mature at the end of their 2nd year, rarely at the end of their 1st year.

Schraetzer *Gymnocephalus schraetzer*
Percidae

Characteristics: body low and elongated, with slimy skin and a relatively large, pointed head which has sensory canals. Dorsal fin undivided. Back and sides yellowish, the upper half of the body with 3-4 black longitudinal lines, which are frequently broken up into streaks and spots. The spiny part of the dorsal fin has rows of dark dots. Average length 15-25 cm, maximum up to 30 cm (250 g).—**Distribution:** only in the Danube region, in the deeper parts of rivers with a sandy or gravelly bottom.—**Habits:** a rather uncommon bottom-living fish which feeds on worms, small crustaceans, insect larvae and fish eggs. After a short migration it spawns in April-May on a gravelly bottom. The sticky eggs adhere to stones and sunken branches. Scarcely anything is known of the further development of the eggs and larvae. Many of its more suitable spawning sites have been lost owing to constructional work and the populations are endangered and steadily decreasing.

Zingel *Aspro zingel* Percidae

Characteristics: body spindle-shaped, almost cylindrical, with a pointed, somewhat triangular head and a ventral mouth. Two dorsal fins, the first with 13-15 spiny rays. Caudal peduncle shorter than the base of the 2nd dorsal fin (c.f. Streber, *Aspro streber*: 1st dorsal fin with 8-9 spiny rays, caudal peduncle thin, cylindrical, about as long as the base of the 2nd dorsal fin). Body yellow-brown with 6-7 irregular, sometimes indistinct transverse bars (Streber has 4-5 sharply defined bars). Belly whitish. Average length 15-20 cm, maximum up to 50 cm.—**Distribution:** Danube and its tributaries, in shallow, running water.—**Habits:** a nocturnal bottom-living fish, spending the day hidden under rocks.—**Diet:** bottom-living invertebrates, fish eggs, taken on the bottom in rapid bursts of speed; it can turn its head to the side and move its eyes independently of one another. Spawns in March-April, each female laying c. 5,000 eggs (1.5 mm diameter) over gravel in a strong current. The populations of Zingel, and particularly of Streber, have been much reduced by disturbance to their habitat.

Small-mouth Black Bass *Micropterus dolomieu*
Centrarchidae

Characteristics: body spindle-shaped, laterally compressed, somewhat high-backed when old, with a large head and wide mouth. Lower jaw protruding, upper jaw extending backwards to below the eye (in the closely related Large-mouth Black Bass, *M. salmoides,* the upper jaw extends behind the eye). Dorsal fin divided by a deep notch, the anterior, spiny part being lower then the posterior. Head and the dorsal fin base with scales. Lateral line with 72-75 scales. Back dark olive-green, sides paler with brownish spots and bands, belly whitish; old individuals uniform dark greenish-grey. Maximum length c. 50 cm.—**Distribution:** U.S.A. (northern Minnesota southwards to Alabama and Oklahoma) in clear, cold, large rivers and lakes. Introduced into Europe since 1883.—**Habits:** predatory and very resistant to water pollution. Spawns in May-June, making a spawning pit (0.3-1 m diameter) in gravel near the bank. The female lays 1,200-1,600 eggs (c. 1 mm diameter) per kg body weight. These adhere to the bottom of the nest and hatch in 8-14 days. The eggs and fry are guarded by the male.

Pumpkinseed   *Lepomis gibbosus*
Centrarchidae

Characteristics: body high-backed, laterally compressed with an undivided dorsal fin. Mouth small, slightly dorsal, the upper jaw extending backwards to below the front edge of the eye. Coloration olive-brown with numerous bluish or greenish iridescent spots, the sides with small yellowish-brown to orange markings. The back of the gill cover with a red spot edged with black. Average length 10-15 cm, maximum up to 30 cm.—**Distribution:** originally North America. Introduced into Europe in the late 19th century, and occasionally seen in England.—**Habits:** prefers fairly warm ponds and lakes and slow-flowing rivers.—**Diet:** worms, small crustaceans (waterfleas), insects and their larvae, fish eggs and fry. Lives during summer in depths of 1-2 m, but in deeper water in winter. Spawning occurs in May-June. The eggs are laid in shallow pits and both they and the fry are guarded by the male who remains above the nest.

Freshwater Blenny   *Blennius fluviatilis*
Blenniidae

Characteristics: body elongated with a naked, slimy skin and long dorsal and anal fins. Ventral fins on the throat, each with 3 fin rays. A short filament above each eye. Males at spawning time with a short keel along the top of the head. Each jaw has a row of well-developed low teeth and large curved "canines". Coloration varying according to population, locality and mood. Back usually olive-brown, sides yellowish-green, belly yellowish-white. Back and sides with round or longish brown markings. Average length 8-10 cm, maximum 15 cm.—**Distribution:** Mediterranean area in clear lakes (e.g. Garda), canals and slow-flowing streams.—**Habits:** an active, very inquisitive bottom-living fish from a primarily marine family that has invaded fresh waters. It lurks under rocks or empty shells in shallow places near the banks. Juveniles are often seen in shoals, adults singly in their territory.—**Diet:** small, bottom-living invertebrates. The eggs (diameter c. 1 mm) are laid under stones and are guarded by the male.

Miller's Thumb   *Cottus gobio*

Cottidae

Characteristics: body club-shaped, scaleless, with a broad flat head. Mouth very wide, terminal. Eyes positioned high up on the head. Gill cover with a powerful, pointed spine. Two dorsal fins, the 1st short and spiny, the 2nd similar to the anal fin. Pectoral fins large, ventral fins positioned on the breast. Lateral line, with 30-35 small scales, running along the sides to the caudal fin base. Swimbladder lacking. Male with a genital papilla. Coloration varying acording to locality; back and sides brownish to grey, frequently with yellow tones, belly white with a mother-of-pearl sheen. Ventral fins white, without transverse bars. Average length 10-15 cm, maximum up to 18 cm.—**Distribution:** Europe, in shallow rivers rich in oxygen and with a strong current, and near the banks of clear, high altitude lakes (up to 2,200 m in the Alps) with sandy and gravelly bottoms.—**Habits:** a bottom-living fish spending the day under stones or roots. When disturbed it dashes about in a zigzag course and soon disappears into its hiding-place. It comes out at twilight to feed on small, bottom-living invertebrates, fish eggs and fry. Spawning occurs in February-May. The courting male, which is darker and more intensely coloured, prepares a small spawning pit under a stone. After a characteristic courtship, the female lays c. 100-200 pale yellow to orange eggs (diameter 2-2.5 mm). These stick together in a clump and are thus prevented from being washed away. They are guarded by the male and hatch in 3-6 weeks, depending upon the temperature. The newly hatched larvae (length 6-7 mm) have a large round yolk sac which provides them with sustenance during a resting period of 10-12 days. The young fish grow very rapidly, and are sexually mature at the end of their 2nd year. In many areas this species has become quite rare, partly because it requires clean water with a gravel bottom. Miller's Thumbs are unpopular because they feed on fish spawn and fry. On the other hand, in some areas they form an important part of the diet of Brown Trout.

Three-spined Stickleback

Gasterosteus aculeatus   Gasterosteidae

Characteristics: back with 3 separate, movable spines. Ventral fins each with a powerful spine. Lateral line covered by bony plates. Back blue-grey to olive-green, sides silvery, belly whitish. At spawning time the males have a blue-green back, red throat and breast, iridescent silvery-blue iris and dark dorsal and anal fins. Usually up to 8 cm, marine migrant forms up to 11 cm.—**Distribution:** Europe, North America, Asia in coastal and inland waters.—**Habits:** an active small fish, feeding on worms, small crustaceans, insect larvae, fish eggs and fry. The marine migrant forms move into fresh water for spawning. The male builds a nest of plant fragments cemented together by a secretion from his kidneys. Spawning occurs in March-July. Each female lays 100-400 eggs which hatch in 4-27 days, depending upon the temperature. The male guards the eggs and later the fry for c. 1 week. The young are sexually mature at the end of their 1st or 2nd year.

Nine-spined Stickleback

Gasterosteus pungitius   Gasterosteidae

Characteristics: more slender and elongated than the preceding species, and with 7-12 dorsal spines. Snout rather blunt. Back dark brownish-grey to greenish-grey, sides paler with slight iridescence, belly whitish to yellowish-green. Back and sides with dark transverse bars. At spawning time the male has a black throat and breast, and orange ventral fins with pale blue rays. Maximum length up to 7 cm.—**Distribution:** Europe (North and Baltic Sea areas, England, Ireland, northern France and eastwards); also in Asia and North America.—**Habits:** lives mostly near the bottom in shallow ponds and ditches, retreating into the mud or under plants when disturbed.—**Diet:** small crustaceans, fish eggs and fry. Spawning occurs in April-July, when the male builds a nest among plants, usually just above the bottom. In contrast to the Three-Spined Stickleback the young do not live in shoals.

Tope *Galeorhinus galeus*
Carcharhinidae

Characteristics: body slender, elongated with a long, very pointed snout. Eyes oval, with a nictitating membrane in the front corner. Teeth triangular, smooth inside, and serrated posteriorly. Five gill slits, the last above the pectoral fins. First dorsal fin 2 to 3 times the length of the 2nd. Caudal fin with a deep notch on the lower edge. Back dark to steel-grey, sides paler, belly white or like mother-of-pearl. Maximum length c. 2 m.—**Distribution:** north-east Atlantic (Iceland to Norway, North Sea to Morocco, Madeira), Mediterranean, in shallow water down to 40-100 m, over sand and gravel bottoms.—**Habits:** lives close to the bottom and is rarely seen in surface waters. In summer it moves singly or in small groups into coastal waters.—**Diet:** small bottom-living fishes and invertebrates. The female gives birth to 20-40 live young (length c. 40 cm) in May-September.

Spur-dog *Squalus acanthias*
Squalidae

Characteristics: body slender and elongated with a pointed snout. Eyes large, oval, without a nictitating membrane. Upper jaw with 24-28, lower jaw with 22-24 teeth. Five gill slits. Two dorsal fins, the first longer than the 2nd, and both with a powerful spine at the front. No anal fin. Caudal fin with a large upper lobe, without a notch. Back pale to dark grey or brownish, sides and belly paler, the back and sides with irregularly distributed white markings which disappear with age. Maximum length c. 1-2 m (10 kg).—**Distribution:** both sides of the North Atlantic in fairly shallow water and down to c. 400 m, exceptionally to 950 m. Also in Mediterranean and Black Sea.—**Habits:** a very common small bottom-living shark, occurring mostly on muddy ground, in shoals of up to 1,000 individuals.—**Diet:** fishes, crustaceans and other invertebrates. The female gives birth to 4-8 living young (length 20-33 cm) after a gestation period of 18-22 months. Males are sexually mature at 60-80 cm, females at 75-90 cm. Longevity 20-24 years.

Lesser Spotted Dogfish   *Scyliorhinus canicula*
Scyliorhinidae

Characteristics: body slender, elongated with a short, rounded snout. Eyes longish-oval with a thick skin fold at the lower edge. Five small gill slits. Two dorsal fins, the first behind the ventral fins, the second behind the anal. Ventral fins pointed at the rear end. Caudal only slightly upturned. Back brown to reddish-brown, grey or yellowish-grey, with brown or black spots, sides paler, belly pale grey or yellowish without markings. Length 60-100 cm.—**Distribution:** northeast Atlantic (southern Norway to Senegal), North Sea, Mediterranean, in depths of 3-110 m around Britain, 20-400 m in the Mediterranean.—**Habits:** active at night and in twilight, usually in large shoals.—**Diet:** small bottom-living invertebrates (worms, molluscs, crustaceans) and small fishes. Spawning time varies according to locality. The female lays 18-20 eggs, each enclosed in a horny capsule (c. 6 cm long) with a long tendril at each corner. These hatch in 8-10 months. Sexually mature at a length of c. 60 cm.

Nursehound   *Scyliorhinus stellaris*
Scyliorhinidae

Characteristics: body stouter with a more rounded snout than in the preceding species. Eyes longish-oval with a thick skin fold at the lower edge. Five small gill slits. Two dorsal fins. Ventral fins with rounded near edges. Caudal peduncle almost straight. Back dark grey, grey-brown to red-brown, sides paler, belly whitish, the back and sides with roundish, brown markings. Maximum length up to c. 1 m.—**Distribution:** east Atlantic (northwards to Norway), Mediterranean, down to depths of 60 m, over rocky ground.—**Habits:** in shallower water and not so common as the preceding species. The egg capsules (3.5 × 10-13 cm) are not so transparent and are probably laid at all times of the year, usually among algae. They hatch in c. 9 months.

Monkfish   *Squatina squatina*

Squatinidae

Characteristics: body much flattened, somewhat skate-like, with a broad head and rounded snout. Nostrils tubular with small barbels. Eyes small, without nictitating membrane, and smaller in diameter than the half-moon shaped spiracles. Pectoral fins broad and wing-like with rounded edges. ventral fins similar but smaller, anal fin lacking. Two dorsal fins on the caudal peduncle, the lower lobe of the caudal fin larger than the upper. Back grey, brownish or greenish, usually with dark marbling, occasionally also with rows of paler markings. Belly whitish. Average length 90-120 cm, maximum up to 2.5 m (80 kg).—**Distribution:** north-east Atlantic (southern Norway to Canaries), Mediterranean, on gravelly or preferably sandy bottoms in depths of 5-100 m.—**Habits:** a bottom-living fish in coastal waters, which often partly buries itself in the sand.—**Diet:** crustaceans, molluscs and small fishes. The female gives birth to 7-25 living young (length c. 20 cm) in shallow waters in the summer (north-east Atlantic) or early spring (Mediterranean).

Marbled Electric Ray   *Torpedo marmorata*

Torpedinidae

Characteristics: body almost circular, with a short caudal peduncle carrying the 2 dorsal fins. Skin smooth, without spines. Eyes small. Spiracles with 6-8 small papillae on their inner edges. Pectoral fins broad, fleshy, forming the outer edge of the body disc. Caudal fin well developed. Each side of the body has a large electric organ, visible through the skin, which can produce 45-220 volts. Back pale to dark brown, with darker marbling, belly whitish with a dark border. Maximum length up to 60 cm.—**Distribution:** north-east Atlantic (southern England to West Africa, rare in the North Sea in summer), Mediterranean, usually on sandy or muddy ground in depths of 2-20 m, only rarely down to 100 m.—**Habits:** a solitary, nocturnal fish, feeding on crustaceans, molluscs and small bottom-living fishes. The prey is covered with the fish's body and paralysed by an electric shock. The female gives birth to 5-20 living young.

Cuckoo Ray *Raja naevus*
Rajidae

Characteristics: body broad and disc-like, with rounded "wing" edges, the front edge of the disc only slightly concave. Snout blunt. Upperside rough, except for a smooth area on each wing. Adults with 4 rows of spines on the caudal peduncle, of which the 2 central rows extend forwards. Juveniles with 1 row of spines on the back of the caudal peduncle. Other spiny areas on the wings, the sides of the head and near the eyes. Underside smooth, except at the front edge. Two dorsal fins very close to one another, near the end of the tail. Back pale brown to grey-brown, with paler markings, and 2 large, black and yellow marbled eye spots. Underside whitish. Maximum length c. 70 cm.—**Distribution:** north-east Atlantic (Norway to Morocco), Mediterranean, on sandy ground in depths of 20-100 m.—**Habits:** a bottom-living fish, feeding on worms, crustaceans, molluscs and fishes. The eggs are laid in brownish, translucent capsules (3.5 × 6-7 cm) which have 1 pair of long and 1 pair of short horns.

Roker *Raja clavata*
Rajidae

Characteristics: body lozenge-shaped, with a short blunt snout and angular wings. Back with numerous large spines, which in the female are also present on the belly. Juveniles and females have a row of spines along the dorsal line and caudal peduncle, males have these only on the latter. Back grey, brown or yellowish, with pale and dark markings, particularly in juveniles. Belly white, with a dark border. Males up to c. 70 cm, females up to 125 cm.—**Distribution:** east Atlantic (including English Channel, North Sea), Mediterranean and parts of the Black Sea, in coastal waters down to 280 m.—**Habits:** a mainly nocturnal fish living on sandy and muddy ground.—**Diet:** crustaceans (crabs, prawns), worms, molluscs, echinoderms and bottom-living fishes. At spawning time, in summer, the adults move into shallow water. The female lays c. 20 eggs, each in a capsule (4-6 × 6-9 cm) with short, hollow horns. These hatch in 4-5 months. Males are sexually mature in their 7th, females in their 9th year. Also known as the Thornback Ray.

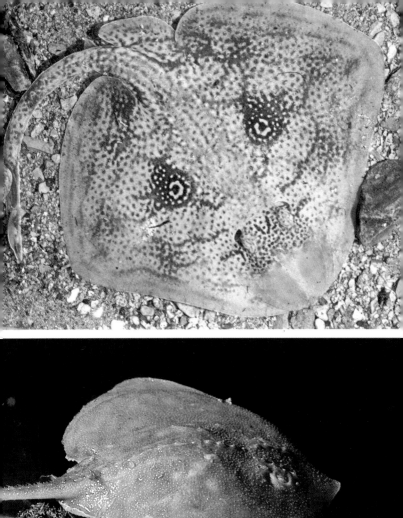

Herring   *Clupea harengus*   Clupeidae

Characteristics: body slender, with an oval cross section, one short dorsal fin and no lateral line. Lower jaw protruding, eyes with transparent fatty lids, gill-covers smooth, without radiating ridges. The dorsal fin starts half way between the snout tip and the caudal peduncle. The ventral fins start just behind the front end of the dorsal fin. The scales between the ventral and anal fins are not sharply keeled. Back dark grey or green, belly silvery. Up to 40 cm long. Longevity 20-25 years.—**Distribution:** mainly in open coastal waters down to 200 m in the North Atlantic: in the west from Greenland to North Carolina, in the east from the Barents Sea to Biscay, also in the North and Baltic Seas.—**Habits:** spends the day mostly in deeper water, rising to the surface at night. Feeding on plankton is mainly by day. There are several races, distinguished by size, growth rate, spawning time and migration routes. The eggs and sperm are released into the water and after fertilization they sink to the bottom. At 9°C they hatch in c. 2 weeks. The larvae (7-9 mm) rise to the surface. Sexual maturity at 3-8 years, depending upon the race.

Pilchard or Sardine   *Sardina pilchardus*
Clupeidae

Characteristics: elongated with a longish oval cross section, one short dorsal fin and no lateral line. Lower jaw protruding, eyes with fatty lids, gill covers with radiating ridges. The dorsal fin starts closer to the snout tip than to the caudal peduncle. The ventral fins are below the rear end of the dorsal fin. The belly edge is not sharply keeled. Back greenish or bluish, belly silvery, flanks with a bluish longitudinal band. Up to c. 26 cm long (at c. 15 years old).—**Distribution:** northeast Atlantic from southern Ireland, southern Britain, North Sea to N.W. Africa; also in the Mediterranean and Black Seas, often in large shoals, at night in depths of 15-35 m, by day 25-55 m. In their coastal migrations they move northwards in summer, southwards in winter.—**Habits:** an openwater, shoaling fish feeding on plankton, fish eggs etc. Spawning occurs in spring to summer, depending upon the water temperature. The free-floating eggs are laid near the coast, and they hatch in 2-4 days into larvae (4 mm long). Sexually mature at 3 years (length 19-20 cm).

Conger Eel   *Conger conger*
Congridae

Characteristics: body stout, snake-like without scales. Mouth
opening wide, extending back to the centre of the eye. Upper
jaw protruding, eye oval, gill opening long, slit-shaped,
reaching down to the ventral surface. Pectoral fins pointed
with 17-20 rays. The dorsal fin starts above the tips of the pectorals. Back grey-brown or blackish, with bluish sheen, belly
whitish. Males usually up to 1 m, females 1.5-2 m, maximum
c. 3 m (65 kg).—**Distribution:** north-east Atlantic (Norway to
Canaries), North and Mediterranean Seas, mainly off rocky
coasts down to at least 2,000 m.—**Habits:** by day usually hidden in rock crevices, by night hunting for prey (fishes, squid,
crustaceans). Believed to spawn in the Atlantic at depths still
unknown. After spawning (3-8 million eggs) the parents die.
The translucent, laterally compressed leptocephalus larvae
spend 1-2 years at depths of 100-200 m, assume the typical eel
shape when 14-16 cm long and move towards the coast.
Sexually mature at 5-15 years.

Moray Eel   *Muraena helena*
Muraenidae

Characteristics: body stout, snake-like without pectoral and
ventral fins. Eyes small, roundish, jaws long, extending back
to far behind the eyes, with long, pointed teeth. Gill opening
small, round. Coloration usually dark brown, with an
irregular yellowish or whitish marbled pattern. Up to 1.5 m
long.—**Distribution:** on rocky coasts in the Mediterranean
and north-east Atlantic (British Isles (rarely) to Senegal) from
shallow water to considerable depths.—**Habits:** in some
places a very abundant predatory fish which divers see peering
out of rocks or sheltering in the amphorae from wrecks.
During the winter months they move into shallower coastal
waters to breed. The eggs float free in the water and thus
become widely distributed. Moray Eels do not have venom
glands associated with the teeth, but they give a dangerous
bite which often becomes infected.

Broad-nosed Pipefish *Syngnathus typhle*

Syngnathidae

Characteristics: body long, thin with an armour of bony plates arranged in rows. Snout tall (more than half the body height), strongly compressed laterally, but rounded in front. Pectoral fins present. Dorsal fin with 29-39 rays, caudal fin pointed. Back green, red or blackish-brown, with white stippling; head with darker spots. Up to 35 cm long.—**Distribution:** non-migratory in shallow water, often among eel-grass, sometimes in brackish water, with 4 subspecies: *S. t. typhle,* European Atlantic coasts (Norway to North Africa), *S. t. rondeletii,* Mediterranean, *S. t. rotundatus,* northern Adriatic and *S. t. argentatus,* Black Sea.—**Habits:** lives among eel-grass, waiting for prey (small crustaceans, fish eggs etc.). Spawns in spring to summer, the female producing 100-250 eggs (diameter 1.7 mm). After a long courtship these are transferred by her elongated genital papilla into a brood pouch on the male's belly. There they remain for about 4 weeks until they hatch into fully formed young, c. 25 mm long.

Snake Pipefish *Entelurus aequoreus*

Syngnathidae

Characteristics: body long, thin, almost cylindrical with an armour of bony plates. No pectoral fins. Caudal fin much reduced, with few tiny rays, dorsal fin with 37-44 rays. Coloration yellowish or brownish-grey, the flanks with numerous silvery transverse bars often with dark edges; a reddish longitudinal band runs from the snout tip through the eye to the gill cover. Males up to 40 cm, females up to 60 cm.—**Distribution:** north Atlantic from Iceland and Norway to Portugal, but not in the Mediterranean, in coastal areas with seaweed at depths of 5-30 m.—**Habits:** lives among seaweeds and feeds on small crustaceans, fish eggs etc. Spawning takes place in June-July, the female laying 400-1,000 eggs (diameter 1.2 mm). These are transferred to the ventral surfaces of several males who carry them around until they hatch into young 11-12 mm long. Newly hatched young still have pectoral fins, but these are lost during development.

Sea-horse   *Hippocampus ramulosus*

Syngnathidae

Characteristics: like the pipefishes the sea-horses have an external armour consisting of rows of bony plates. In contrast to their relatives, however, the sea-horses have the head bent at an angle to the body and a tail modified to form a prehensile organ, which can grip plants. The eyes can move independently of one another. The snout is in the form of an elongated tube, with the small mouth at its tip. The dorsal fin is well developed, the pectoral and anal fins are small and ventral and caudal fins are lacking. The species illustrated is distinguished by its long snout (over 1/3 the head length). In the Short-nosed Sea-horse, *H. hippocampus,* the snout is scarcely 1/3 of the head length. The dorsal armour consists of 40-50 body rings; the head and back carry fleshy strands. Coloration greenish or brownish, sometimes with fine white dots on the edges of the body rings. Up to 12 cm long.—**Distribution:** in shallow waters with seaweeds and eelgrass, in the Mediterranean and Black Sea and along the North Atlantic coasts from Ireland and the southern North Sea (rare) southwards to West Africa, Madeira and the Canaries.—**Habits:** sea-horses are rather difficult to observe underwater, because their shape and coloration are so well matched to the seaweeds around them. They can remain almost motionless with the tail coiled round a piece of weed. They swim slowly and in an erect posture, with the help of the undulating movements of the dorsal fin. In catching their prey (plankton, fish eggs) the tubular snout acts like a pipette, sucking the food in. Sea-horses practice brood protection. The males carry the eggs in a brood pouch on their belly until they hatch. Breeding takes place in May-July. Mating starts with a mature male showing his brood pouch to a passing female. After a complicated courtship the transfer of the eggs usually begins at twilight. Both sexes rise to the surface belly to belly. The eggs are deposited in a brood pouch on the male's belly by the female's short genital papilla and remain in there for 4-5 weeks. They are then expelled as tiny miniatures of the parents, by pumping movements of the male's body.

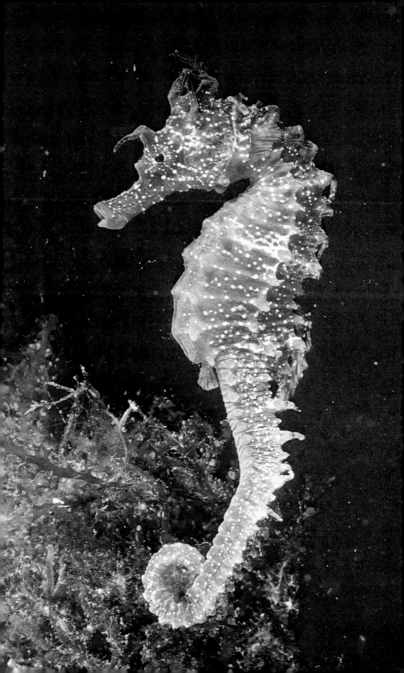

Cod   *Gadus morhua*
Gadidae

Characteristics: body elongated with 3 rounded dorsal and 2 anal fins. Upper jaw protruding. Chin barbel long, almost as long as the eye diameter. Lateral line pale and conspicuous, curved upwards at the front, becoming straight at the rear. The 1st anal fin starts below or just behind the front of the 2nd dorsal fin, the rear edge of the caudal fin is straight. Coloration usually greenish, brownish or reddish with various markings, the belly off-white. Average length 80-100 cm, maximum c. 150 cm (40 kg).—**Distribution:** north Atlantic from North Carolina to Greenland, from Biscay to Spitsbergen. In addition to the stocks that migrate for spawning and feeding purposes there are also non-migratory populations.—**Habits:** omnivorous. Most populations spawn in spring at 4-6°C. Eggs and sperm are shed at random, the number of eggs being 500,000 to 5 million. The transparent eggs (diameter 1.5 mm) rise to the surface and hatch in 2-4 weeks. After 3-5 months the 3-6 cm juveniles move to the bottom. The age of sexual maturity varies according to the race.

Haddock   *Melanogrammus aeglefinus*
Gadidae

Characteristics: with 3 dorsal and 2 anal fins. Upper jaw protruding, chin barbel very short, lateral line black, only slightly curved. First anal fin starts below the front end of the 2nd dorsal fin; rear edge of caudal fin is concave. Back dark purple to black, sometimes olive-green, flanks dark and shiny, belly whitish. A conspicuous black spot above each pectoral fin. Up to 100 cm long (12 kg).—**Distribution:** north Atlantic from North Carolina to Greenland, and from Portugal to Iceland, North and White Seas, usually close to the bottom in depths of 10-300 m.—**Habits:** feeds on bottom-living invertebrates, small fishes, fish eggs. Spawns in March-June, the females producing 100,000 to 1 million eggs, which float, as do the larvae. In autumn the juveniles (7-15 cm long) move down to the bottom. Sexually mature at 3-4 years (30-40 cm).

Bib   *Trisopterus luscus*
Gadidae

Characteristics: body tall with 3 dorsal and 2 anal fins. Chin barbel as long as the eye diameter, upper jaw somewhat protruding, lateral line golden-yellow, much curved. Anus below the middle of the 1st dorsal fin. Coloration pale coppery, with 4-5 broad, dark transverse bands. A small dark marking at the insertion of each pectoral fin. Rear edge of the caudal fin black. Usually up to 30 cm long, maximum c. 40 cm.—**Distribution:** north-east Atlantic (British Isles and North Sea to Morocco) in moderate depths off the coast, in north-west Mediterranean in 250-300 m (spawning at 50 m).—**Habits:** feeds mainly on molluscs and crustaceans, with increasing age on fishes and squid. Juveniles live close to the coast, adults in deeper water. Spawning occurs in March-April, sometimes as late as August, usually at depths of 50-100 m with a temperature of 8-9°C. Eggs and larvae float near the surface.

Whiting   *Merlangius merlangus*
Gadidae

Characteristics: body elongated with 3 dorsal and 2 anal fins. Upper jaw protruding, teeth pointed, chin barbel tiny or absent, lateral line bronze-coloured, slightly curved. The long 1st anal fin starts below the middle of the 1st dorsal fin. Caudal fin broad with a straight rear edge. Back olive, sand-coloured or bluish, flanks silvery with golden spots or stripes, belly whitish. A dark marking at the insertion of each pectoral fin. In North Sea seldom over 40 cm long, maximum up to 70 cm.—**Distribution:** north-east Atlantic from Iceland, Faeroes and northern Norway to Biscay, also North Sea and western Baltic, over sandy and muddy bottoms from coastal waters to 200 m. Larvae and juveniles are frequently seen under the umbrella of a jellyfish.—**Habits:** feeds on crustaceans and fishes. Spawns in January (Biscay) to June (Iceland) at 5-10°C in depths of 30-100 m. Eggs and larvae float free in the water. Juveniles move to the bottom when 5-10 cm long. Sexually mature at 3-4 years.

Pollack   *Pollachius pollachius*
Gadidae

Characteristics: body elongated with 3 dorsal and 2 anal fins distinctly separated from one another. Lower jaw protruding, particularly in older individuals, without a chin barbel, lateral line greenish-brown, curving upwards above the pectoral fins, then running straight. The long 1st anal fin starts below the middle of the 1st dorsal fin. Caudal fin broad, concave. Back usually brownish or olive, flanks yellowish, often with dark yellow or orange spots or stripes. Usually up to 80 cm, maximum up to 120 cm long (over 15 years old).—**Distribution:** north-east Atlantic from North Cape and south-east Iceland to Biscay, also North Sea and (rarely) northern Mediterranean, from coastal waters to depths of 200 m.—**Habits:** feeds on crustaceans (prawns etc) and fishes such as Sand-eels, Herring, Sprat and small Cod. Pollack spawn in shallower water than Saithe, usually in less than 100 m, and prefer a somewhat higher temperature (c. 8-10°C). Eggs and larvae float free in the water.

Saithe   *Pollachius virens*
Gadidae

Characteristics: also known as Coalfish or Coley. Body steamlined with 3 dorsal and 2 anal fins, all clearly separated. Lower jaw somewhat protruding in larger individuals, chin barbel very small or absent, lateral line pale and almost straight. The front end of the 1st anal fin is immediately below the front end of the 2nd dorsal fin. Caudal fin broad, concave. Back greenish-brown to blackish-brown, belly silvery white. Maximum up to 120 cm (27 years old).—**Distribution:** north Atlantic (Greenland to Chesapeake Bay, and Barents Sea, Spitsbergen, Iceland, Britain to Biscay; also in the North Sea).—**Habits:** the young feed on crustaceans and fish spawn, the adults almost exclusively on shoaling fishes (Herring, Sprat) which they often pursue over long distances. Spawning takes place in spring (North Sea, in 100-200 m at 3-10°C). Eggs and larvae float free in the water and are carried by currents into coastal waters where the young remain for 2-3 years. They are sexually mature at the end of their 5th-10th year.

Scad   *Trachurus trachurus*

Carangidae

Characteristics: body long, slender, with a pointed snout. Mouth wide, oblique, the jaws extending to below the eyes which are large, with transparent fatty lids. Scales small, easily rubbed off, lateral line curved, with 69-79 tall bony scutes. First dorsal fin spiny, taller than the very long 2nd dorsal; 2 free spines in front of the anal fin. Pectoral fins long and, when laid back, reaching to the anal; caudal fin cleft. Back grey or blue-green, sides silvery with a metallic sheen, belly silvery-white, gill covers with small dark spots. Maximum length c. 40 cm.—**Distribution:** eastern Atlantic (Norway), North Sea, Mediterranean, Black Sea, in open water at depths of 10-100 m.—**Habits:** a shoaling fish feeding on crustaceans, squid and small fishes. Spawning takes place in November-March (North Sea May-June) when the female lays 3,000-139,000 eggs that float in the plankton. Young fish (1-2.5 cm) are frequently seen in small shoals beneath jellyfishes or near flotsam. They are sexually mature at the end of their 2nd year.

Bass   *Dicentrarchus labrax*

Serranidae

Characteristics: body elongated, spindle-shaped with a relatively long head (5-6 times the eye diameter). Rear end of pre-operculum (front bone of the gill cover) with large teeth. Scales small, 65-80 in a longitudinal row. Two dorsal fins of equal length, the 1st with 8-9 spiny rays. Anal fin with 3 spiny rays, caudal fin slightly concave. Coloration silvery, back grey, sides paler, belly whitish. Young fish up to c. 10 cm long have black dots on the upper half of the body. Maximum length c. 100 cm (5-7 kg).—**Distribution:** north-east Atlantic (Norway to Senegal and Canaries), southern North Sea, Mediterranean and Black Seas, on rocky coasts, from near the surface to c. 100 m. Moves away from the coasts in winter.—**Habits:** adults are solitary, feeding almost exclusively on fishes. The young live in small shoals and feed mainly on worms, crustaceans, squid and small fishes. Spawning takes place in January-March in the Mediterranean, March-June in the English Channel, May-August in the north. The eggs are free-floating.

Painted Comber   *Serranus scriba*
Serranidae

Characteristics: body longish-oval, with small ctenoid scales (one edge with comb-like teeth). Gill cover with 2 spines, the rear end of its front bone (pre-operculum) toothed. One long, undivided dorsal fin, the front part with 10 spiny rays. Anal fin with 3 spiny rays. Back and sides reddish or yellowish-brown, with 4-7 dark transverse bars, some divided. Belly with large blue or violet markings. Head with blue and red marks resembling Arabic script. Maximum length c. 25 cm.—**Distribution:** east Atlantic coasts from Biscay to South Africa, Mediterranean and Black Seas, in shallow coastal waters (usually less than 30 m depth) over rocky ground with algae.—**Habits:** a solitary species which takes up a territory and defends it against others of its own species.—**Diet:** mainly small shoaling fishes, and also crustaceans and molluscs. This is a hermaphrodite species which can produce ripe sperm and eggs at the same time. Spawning is in May-August and the eggs adhere to rocks near the coast.

Dusky Perch   *Epinephelus guaza*
Serranidae

Characteristics: body longish-oval with small ctenoid scales extending on to the head. Gill cover with 3 short spines, the rear edge of its front bone (pre-operculum) toothed. Jaws with long, powerful, pointed teeth, the lower jaw slightly protruding and scaled. One long, undivided dorsal fin, its front part with 11 spiny rays. Anal fin with 3 spiny rays. Back greenish-brown, sides paler, belly yellowish. Greenish-yellow marbling and bands on the head, back and sides. Dorsal fin with an orange border, the other fins with pale edges. Maximum length c. 140 cm.—**Distribution:** east Atlantic from Biscay to South Africa (very rarely off England and Ireland), Mediterranean and west Atlantic from the Guianas to Brazil, off rocky coasts in depths of 8-200 m.—**Habits:** these are solitary fish, each with a clearly defined territory which must have a number of hiding-places. They swim very well but spend much of their time in front of or in their retreat. They spawn in summer, sometimes evidently at the full moon, and the eggs are free-floating.

Brown Meagre   *Sciaena umbra*   Sciaenidae

Characteristics: body high-backed with a rounded head profile and stumpy snout. Mouth wide, extending to the rear edge of the eyes. Scales relatively large. Two dorsal fins connected by a very thin skin fold, the 2nd twice as long as the 1st. Anal fin with 2 spiny rays, the 2nd of which is stout. Rear edge of caudal fin almost straight in adults, slightly indented in the young. Back and sides brownish-bronze with a golden sheen, belly paler with a silvery sheen. Fins dark, the spiny rays of the ventral and anal fins white. Average length 40 cm, maximum c. 70 cm.—**Distribution:** north-east Atlantic (southern Biscay to Senegal), Mediterranean and Black Seas, among rocks and eel-grass at depths of 5-20 m.—**Habits:** a mainly nocturnal species, usually living in small shoals. During the day they are frequently found in their retreats and scarcely moving. They feed on small fishes, crustaceans and molluscs. Spawning takes place in late spring and early summer.

Red Mullet   *Mullus surmuletus*   Mullidae

Characteristics: body elongated, laterally compressed with large scales. Head profile fairly steep, convex. Eyes large, at the edge of the head. Lower jaw with 2 long, movable barbels, cheek with 2 large scales below the eye. Two widely separate dorsal fins, the 1st with 7-8 spiny rays. Coloration yellowish-brown to red, varying according to season, age and depth; scales with dark edges. By day, particularly when shoaling, Red Mullet have dark red to brown longitudinal stripes running from the eye to the caudal fin and 4-5 yellow longitudinal bands. At night this pattern disappears, leaving a faint marbling. Average length 20 cm, maximum c. 40 cm.—**Distribution:** north-east Atlantic (Scotland to Canaries), Mediterranean; rare at Bergen in Norway and in the western Baltic. Adults live over sandy or muddy ground at depths of 3-90 m, young fish in shallow water off rocky coasts.—**Habits:** feeds on bottom-living animals which they detect with the barbels. Red Mullet live singly or in shoals of up to 50 individuals. Spawning takes place in July-September in depth of 10-55 m. The larvae are planktonic. Sexually mature at 4 years.

Saddled Bream   *Oblada melanura*

Sparidae

Characteristics: body oval, laterally compressed with a slightly convex head profile. Mouth oblique, lips soft, upper and lower jaws equal in length, each with several rows of teeth. The outermost row has cutting teeth in the front, pointed, wedge-shaped teeth at the sides and 4 rows of small grinding teeth at the back. Dorsal fin undivided, the front part with 11 spiny rays, the rear with 14 soft rays. Anal fin with 3 spiny and 13-14 soft rays. Coloration silvery with indistinct dark longitudinal stripes and a characteristic large dark marking with a white border on the caudal peduncle. Maximum length up to 30 cm.—**Distribution:** east Atlantic (Biscay to Angola), Mediterranean, usually over rocky ground.—**Habits:** lives in small shoals at 2-3 m and in more open water than other sea bream. Spawns in late spring. The larvae drift in the plankton until late summer.

Black Sea Bream   *Spondyliosoma cantharus*

Sparidae

Characteristics: body high-backed, laterally compressed, the adult males almost disc-shaped with a concave forehead, the young fish (10-15 cm) with a convex forehead and pointed snout. Mouth small, not reaching to below the front edge of the eye. Each jaw with 1 row of small, pointed, slightly curved teeth, the front ones somewhat larger. Dorsal fin undivided, with 11 spiny and 12-13 soft rays. Anal fin with 3 spiny and 9-11 soft rays. Coloration very variable. In young fish (up to c. 20 cm) the back is grey to yellowish, the sides silvery with numerous longitudinal lines, the fins sometimes with white spots, the caudal with a broad dark border. Adults are dark to blue-grey, frequently with 6-9 paler transverse bars on the sides, males ready to spawn having an iridescent blue-green band between the eyes. Maximum length up to 50 cm.—**Distribution:** east Atlantic (Norway to Angola), Mediterranean, along rocky coasts, the adults over sandy ground and eel-grass down to 15 m.—**Habits:** spawns in April-May, the male making a depression (diameter 30-100 cm) in sandy ground. The eggs adhere to the bottom of this nest and are guarded by the male. They hatch in c. 9 days and the fry remain in the vicinity until they are 7-8 cm long.

Cuckoo Wrasse   *Labrus mixtus*

Labridae

Characteristics: body elongated with one undivided dorsal fin which has spiny rays in front and soft rays in the shorter rear part. Mouth relatively wide with fleshy lips and protrusible jaws with powerful teeth. Edge of the pre-operculum smooth. Lateral line running parallel to the back, with 50-60 scales. Coloration of sexually mature fish strikingly different. Males (opposite, above) have a bright blue head with dark bands which extend on to the yellow or orange sides, no dark markings on the back, and at spawning time a white spot on the forehead. Females (opposite, below) are yellow or reddish-orange with 3 dark markings on the back (2 below the soft rays of the dorsal fin, 1 on the caudal peduncle, often with white areas in between them, giving a very striking pattern). Males up to 35 cm, females to 30 cm.—**Distribution:** north-east Atlantic (Norway to Senegal), Mediterranean, on rocky coasts, over gravelly bottoms and among eel-grass, in depths of 1-200 m.—**Habits:** like all wrasses these are active swimmers, but only during the day as they hide away in holes and crevices at night. They live for a relatively long time, and there is a record of a specimen 28 cm long which was about 17 years old.—**Diet:** mainly bottom-living invertebrates, such as worms, crustaceans (crabs, barnacles) and molluscs (snails, bivalves). Like many members of this family they can change sex; old females with the typical coloration can become sexually mature and functional males. They show complex behaviour in establishing and defending a territory, in making a nest and in courtship. Spawning takes place in summer. The male makes a nest in his territory, as a depression in the substrate, from which he chases any other males that come too close. By vigorous courtship display he then entices nearby females into the nest to lay their eggs, which he immediately fertilizes. The eggs and for a period the fry are guarded and tended by the male.Later the young fish move into shallow coastal waters among seaweeds.

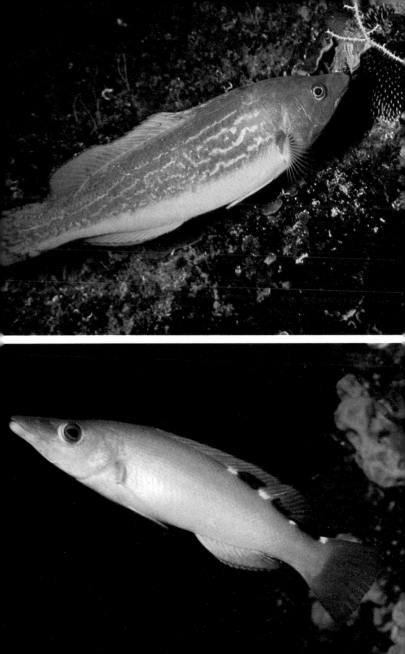

Ballan Wrasse *Labrus bergylta*
Labridae

Characteristics: body elongated, powerful, with a large head, fleshy lips and 1 row of wedge-shaped teeth on each jaw. Edge of pre-operculum smooth. Lateral line parallel to the dorsal line, with 41-47 scales. No difference in coloration between the sexes. Basic coloration variable, usually greenish-brown, each scale with a pale marking and dark border. Juveniles often emerald-green. Rarely over 40 cm, maximum c. 60 cm.—**Distribution:** north-east Atlantic (Norway to Morocco and Canaries), western Mediterranean, off steep, rocky coast in depths of 1-50 m.—**Habits:** active by day, hiding away in holes and crevices at night. Old individuals often seen near their hiding-places, and juveniles occasionally occur in rock pools.—**Diet:** small crustaceans and molluscs which they take from the rocks. The male makes a nest in gravel and spawning takes place in May-July.

Peacock Wrasse *Thalassoma pavo*
Labridae

Characteristics: body elongated with a long dorsal fin, which has only 8 spiny rays in the front part. Mouth small, with a row of small, pointed teeth on each jaw. Scales relatively large. Lateral line with a sharp upward curve at the rear end, and with 26-31 scales. Coloration very variable. Adult males green on the sides with red and blue transverse bars from the front end of the dorsal fin to the ventral fins; head dark red with blue lines. Adult females and juveniles are moss-green with paler transverse bars and a black spot below the dorsal fin approximately in the middle of the body. Maximum length c. 20 cm.—**Distribution:** north-east Atlantic (Biscay to Guinea) and Mediterranean, off rocky coasts with algae and among eel-grass, in depths of 1-50 m.—**Habits:** a warmth-loving species, mainly active during summer when the free-floating eggs are laid. Sex reversal has been recorded, and transitional phases between male and female are not uncommon.

Rainbow Wrasse   *Coris julis*

Labridae

Characteristics: body elongated with a long, pointed snout.
Dorsal and anal fins long, the dorsal having 8-9 spiny rays, of
which the front 2-3 are elongated in the male. Eyes small,
teeth sharp, pointed, the front ones curved forwards. Scales
very small, 73-80 along the lateral line which curves sharply
upwards towards the rear end; cheeks without scales. The
sexes can be distinguished in mature individuals. Adult males
(opposite, above) have a black and orange marking on the anterior, elongated dorsal fin rays, an orange zigzag band along
the sides and a black wedge-shaped marking behind the pectoral fins (this is the *julis* phase). Females (opposite, below)
and juveniles having a bluish marking on each gill cover, and
a pale longitudinal band running from the tip of the snout to
the caudal fin (*giofredi* phase). There are also intermediate
colour phases in those fish changing from female to male.
Males up to 25 cm long, females up to 18 cm.—**Distribution:**
north-east Atlantic (Biscay to Guinea), Mediterranean and
southern Black Sea, near rocky coasts with algae and over eel-
grass; rarely seen north of the English Channel.—**Habits:**
usually living in small shoals. Juveniles act as "cleaners",
that is, they have been seen to take parasites from other
fishes. Only active by day, for at the onset of twilight they
bury themselves in the sand where they spend the night. They
also hide in the substrate when threatened by enemies.—**Diet:**
mainly small crustaceans and molluscs; they can crush such
hard-shelled prey with the fused pharyngeal teeth. Spawning
takes place in early summer, when the males become particularly brightly coloured. The eggs contain an oil globule
which enables them to float in the water. They hatch in 1-2
days and the newly hatched fry also float. Sex reverrsal occurs
in some older individuals. After a long female phase and a
very short transitional phase the fish have a long male phase.

Demoiselle   *Chromis chromis*
Pomacentridae

Characteristics: body oval, laterally compressed with a forked tail. Mouth small, terminal, positioned obliquely. Scales very large, and 24-30 in the lateral line. Dorsal fin undivided, the posterior soft rays taller than the spiny rays. Young fish up to 10 mm long have shiny blue stripes on the head and sides. Adults dark brown with dark-edged scales. Maximum length c. 15 cm.—**Distribution:** east Atlantic coasts from Portugal to Angola, and Mediterranean, seldom below 25 m, usually over rocks near the coast.—**Habits:** often living in large shoals.—**Diet:** small planktonic animals. The males select territories close to rocky outcrops or over eel-grass in depths of 2-15 m. In June-July the females are led by courtship to the spawning site, which may be a previously cleaned rock. The eggs adhere by filaments to the substrate and are fanned and guarded by the male. The bright blue young fish live in shoals in depressions in the bottom or in protected rock crevices where they can be seen from August onwards.

Greater Weever   *Trachinus draco*
Trachinidae

Characteristics: body elongated, laterally compressed with a large head and a wide obliquely positioned mouth. Eyes high on the head and directed upwards; in contrast to the Lesser Weever (*T. vipera)* there is a small spine at the front edge of the eye. Each gill cover has a long spine with a venom gland. First dorsal fin short, with 5-7 venomous spines, 2nd dorsal and anal fins very long, ventral fins on the throat. Back yellowish-brown, belly paler, sides with transverse stripes, 1st dorsal fin black. Average length 20-30 cm, maximum c. 42 cm.—**Distribution:** north-east Atlantic (Norway to Morocco, Madeira), Mediterranean, over sandy ground in depths of 5 (rarely) to 150 m. Usually lives in fairly shallow water in summer, moving deeper in autumn.—**Habits:** spends the day buried in the sand, with only the eyes and the 1st dorsal's venom spines visible.—**Diet:** prawns, gobies, dragonets, which they lie in wait for. Spawning takes place in June-July, and the eggs (diameter c. 1 mm) float in the water. The venomous spines can inflict very painful wounds.

Dragonet   *Callionymus lyra*   Callionymidae

Characteristics: body slender, scaleless, with the front part
flattened. Head flat, triangular from above, eyes large. Snout
long, 1½-2½ times the eye length. Mouth small with thick
lips and a very protrusible upper jaw. Gill opening very small,
roundish, positioned high up on the body. Two dorsal fins
close to one another, the 1st short with 4 flexible spiny rays,
which are much elongated in sexually mature males. Ventral
fins well developed, roundish, positioned in front of pectoral
fins. Males usually yellowish or brownish, with bluish stripes
and spots on the body and fins, females with uniformly
coloured fins, 6 greenish or brownish spots on the sides and 3
dark markings on the back. Males up to 30 cm, females up to
20 cm.—**Distribution:** north-east Atlantic, Mediterranean, on
sandy and muddy ground down to depths of 200 m.—**Habits:**
lives on the bottom, often buried in sand or hidden under
stones or shells.—**Diet:** small invertebrates. Spawning occurs
in January-August, depending upon the locality. The male
has a courtship display and during spawning the pair rise to
the surface, with bodies close to one another. The eggs and
larvae float in the plankton, and the young move down to the
bottom when c. 10 mm long. Longevity: males up to 5,
females to 7 years.

Thick-lipped Grey Mullet   *Crenimugil labrosus*
Mugilidae

Characteristics: body spindle-shaped, with large scales. Head
flattened above, mouth small, terminal, upper lip thick with
usually 3 rows of small papillae in older individuals. Two
widely separated dorsal fins, the 1st with 4 spiny rays. Sides
with dark longitudinal stripes. Maximum length up to c. 60
cm (weight 4-5 kg).—**Distribution:** north-east Atlantic
(Iceland, Norway to Senegal, Madeira, Azores),
Mediterranean, near the coast, sometimes in brackish water
and estuaries.—**Habits:** moves northwards in small shoals
during the summer. The young fish feed on planktonic
animals, the adults on small bottom-living invertebrates and
algae which they scrape from the bottom or filter out of the
mud. Spawning takes place in December-March
(Mediterranean) or January-April (Biscay).

114

Characteristics: body elongated, slender, scaled (except the gill cover), with a steep head profile. Three dorsal fins, of which the 1st with 3 spiny rays can be erected independently of the other two. Second dorsal with 1-3 elongated, filamentous rays in sexually mature males. Mouth terminal, eye tentacle short, not branched. Ventral fins positioned on throat. Males red or orange, with a dark head and dark transverse bands, cheeks with sky-blue dots, the rear edge of the 1st dorsal with blackish-red markings, the 2nd and 3rd dorsals with a blue border; at breeding time the head and iris are deep black. Females yellowish-brown, with dark bands, the throat and cheeks citron-yellow.—**Distribution:** north-east Atlantic (northern France to Canaries), Mediterranean, Black Sea, on rocky coasts down to 12 m, especially in shady places, with few seaweeds.—**Habits:** an active bottom-living fish which can move fast when alarmed. Spawning takes place in May-July, when the male defends a territory (diameter c. 1 m) and displays with extended fins to nearby females. The latter spawn with several males.

Tompot Blenny *Blennius gattorugine* Blenniidae

Characteristics: body moderately elongated, laterally compressed, with a rounded head profile. Skin scaleless, slimy. Eyes positioned high on the head, mouth wide, extending to below the centre of the eye, teeth small and pointed, in 1 row, eye tentacle large and branched. Dorsal fin long, without a distinct notch, anal fin with 1 small spiny ray, ventral fins on the throat, filamentous. Coloration yellow-, olive- or reddish-brown, with 6-7 dark transverse bars which continue on to the dorsal and anal fins. Eyes red-brown. Average length c. 20 cm, maximum up to 30 cm.—**Distribution:** north-east Atlantic (northern Scotland and eastern English Channel to West Africa), Mediterranean, in shallow water on rocky ground, extending into the brown seaweed zones in the northern part of the range.—**Habits:** an inquisitive bottom-living fish which disappears into rock crevices when alarmed. Spawning occurs in spring, the eggs being laid under stones. They are guarded by the male who fans fresh water over them with his fins. They hatch after c. 4 weeks and the larvae live at first in the open water, moving down to the bottom as young fish in the summer.

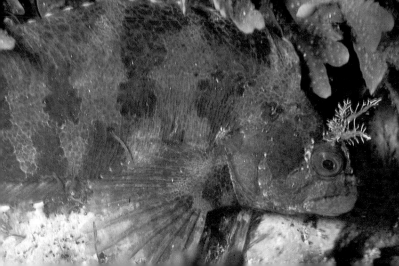

Butterfish *Pholis gunnellus*
Pholidae

Characteristics: body elongated, laterally compressed with very slimy skin, a small head with rounded snout and fleshy lips. Scales very small, lateral line absent. Dorsal fin very long, low, with spiny rays, anal fin half as long as dorsal, ventral fins reduced with only 1 spiny and 1 soft ray. Coloration grey-brown, young fish with irregular dark transverse bars, adults with dark marbling and 9-13 dark markings edged with white along the insertion of the dorsal fin. A dark stripe runs down from the eye to the corner of the mouth. Maximum length up to 25 cm.—**Distribution:** both sides of Atlantic, in the east from the Arctic Sea to the North Sea and English Channel, on muddy, sandy and rocky ground from the tidal zone down to 100 m or more.—**Habits:** a small fish that feeds on worms, crustaceans, molluscs and other bottom-living invertebrates. Spawning occurs in winter, the eggs being laid in nests at depths down to 25 m, and guarded, usually by the female. During this time the parent fish do not feed.

Wolf-fish *Anarhichas lupus*
Anarhichadidae

Characteristics: body elongated, with a large, squat head and broad mouth. Upper and lower jaws with large, curved teeth and the palate and the rear part of the lower jaw with powerful, flat crushing teeth. One long dorsal fin with spiny rays and 1 short anal fin with soft rays. Ventral fins absent. Coloration grey, brownish red or greenish, with dark transverse bars that extend on to the dorsal fin. Maximum length up to 120 cm.—**Distribution:** both sides of the Atlantic, in the west from Greenland to Cape Cod, in the east from the Arctic Sea to Biscay, in depths down to 430 m, preferably on rocky ground, with water temperatures in the range -1° to +14°C.—**Habits:** the powerful dentition enables these fish to feed on hard-shelled bottom-living animals. Spawning takes place in October-January, and the female lays 3,000-24,000 yellowish eggs (diameter 5-6 mm) among stones and seaweed at depths of 40-200 m. They hatch in 2 months and the larvae live in the open water. They become sexually mature at the end of their 6th-7th year when 50-60 cm long.

Black Goby *Gobius niger*
Gobiidae

Characteristics: body relatively elongated, almost cylindrical with a rounded head, bulging cheeks and the eyes close to one another. Two dorsal fins, the 1st with 5-7 (usually 6) spiny rays, which are elongated in the male. Pectoral fins large, with short, free rays in the upper part, ventral fins fused together, forming a suction disc. Usually 35-41 scales in a longitudinal row. Maximum length up to 18 cm.—**Distribution:** north-east Atlantic (Trondheim to Mauritania), Baltic, Mediterranean, Black Sea, in coastal waters over sandy or muddy ground and among eel-grass down to 75 m; also in estuaries and lagoons.—**Habits:** a bottom-living fish, feeding on worms, small crustaceans, molluscs and small fishes. Spawning occurs in March-May (Mediterranean), May-August (Baltic). The male establishes a territory in which he makes a nest under stones or shells and displays to attract the females. The 1,000-6,000 pear-shaped eggs (diameter 0.8 mm) adhere by short filaments to the nest roof and are guarded by the male who fans fresh water over them with his fins. The larvae swim free in the plankton after they have consumed the yolk sac contents, and move down to the bottom when 9 mm long. Sexual maturity at the end of 1-2 years.

Eelpout *Zoarces viviparus*
Zoarcidae

Characteristics: body eel-like with a large, scaleless head. The long dorsal, anal and caudal fins are continuous. Ventral fins small, on the throat. Back yellow-green to yellowish-brown, belly whitish to grey, the head and back with dark markings, the sides with rows of spots along the middle, the dorsal fin with dark transverse bars, the pectorals with a yellow to orange border, which in the male becomes pale red at spawning time. Up to 45 cm long.—**Distribution:** White Sea to eastern English Channel, northern Irish Sea, Baltic, in shallow coastal waters and estuaries at depths of 4-10 m, occasionally down to 40 m.—**Habits:** lives hidden among eel-grass and under rocks or lies buried in soft ground.—**Diet:** worms, small crustaceans, molluscs, fishes. The eggs are fertilized internally and after a period of c. 4 months the female gives birth to up to 400 living young.

Redfish   *Sebastes marinus*

Scorpaenidae

Characteristics: body perch-like and deep red, with large eyes. Interior of mouth pale red, lower jaw smooth. Lateral line with 80-90 scales. Male with a prominent genital papilla. Maximum length c. 100 cm (15 kg, 60 years old).—**Distribution:** both sides of the Atlantic, in the west from Greenland to Cape Cod, in the east from the White Sea to Spitsbergen, Iceland, Norway and Scotland, living near the bottom in coastal waters, preferably over rocky ground and also in the open sea.—**Habits:** young fish feed on luminescent prawns and other crustaceans, arrow-worms, cod eggs, the adults mainly on Herring and Capelin. In the northern Barents Sea mating takes place in October-November. The females then migrate during the winter months to their spawning grounds (including Lofotens, Iceland, Newfoundland) where in April-July in depths of 200-500 m at 4.0-8.5°C they each give birth to 37,000-350,000 young. At birth the larvae are 5-7 mm and they live near the surface. As they grow older they move deeper and at a length of 6 cm they go to the bottom. Sexual maturity at 11 years (length c. 38 cm).

Norway Haddock   *Sebastes viviparus*

Scorpaenidae

Characteristics: body perch-like, red, with indistinct dark transverse bars. Mouth cavity pale red, lower jaw smooth. Lateral line with 70-80 scales. Males with a prominent genital papilla. Average length 20-30 cm.—**Distribution:** both sides of the Atlantic, in the east from the Lofotens and Iceland to the Atlantic coasts of Ireland, over rocky ground in depths of 10-300 m.—**Habits:** a bottom-living fish, mainly in coastal waters. Depending upon her size a female produces 12,000-30,000 living young, which spend the first part of their lives in the plankton. The related Bluemouth, *Helicolenus dactylopterus,* occurs from Norway, Scotland and Ireland to southern Africa and also in the Mediterranean, in depths down to 960 m. It is characterized by a blue mouth cavity and 8 partly free pectoral fin rays.

Red Scorpionfish   *Scorpaena scrofa*
Scorpaenidae

Characteristics: body robust, somewhat laterally compressed
with a large, broad head armed with spines. Eyes relatively
small, oval, mouth very wide. Tentacle above each eye small
and very short. Chin with numerous skin processes. Scales
relatively large. Lateral line with 35-40 scales. Dorsal fin with
spiny rays (with venom glands at the base) separated by a
distinct notch from the short rear part which has soft rays.
Pectoral fins large, anal fin with 3 spiny rays. Coloration
usually reddish-brown with pale and dark marbling, the centre of the dorsal fin often with black markings. Average
length 20-25 cm, maximum c. 50 cm.—**Distribution:** north-
east Atlantic (British Isles to Senegal), Mediterranean, in depths down to 20 m, only over rocky ground.—**Habits:** active in
twilight and at night, remaining motionless and solitary by
day. Spawning occurs in late spring and summer, the eggs
being laid in a transparent gelatinous clump.

Lesser Red Scorpionfish   *Scorpaena notata*
Scorpaenidae

Characteristics: body stocky, somewhat laterally compressed,
with a large, broad head armed with spines. Mouth very wide,
eyes large and round. Tentacle above each eye small, very
short. Chin without skin processes. Scales rather large, 36-40
in the lateral line. Dorsal fin with the spiny part (with venom
glands at the bases of the rays) separated by a notch from the
soft rays. Pectoral fins large, broad, anal fin with 3 spiny
rays. Coloration red, with variable marbling, frequently with
dark dots on the dorsal, caudal and anal fins. Always with a
black spot between the 8th and 10th dorsal fin ray. Maximum
length c. 18 cm.—**Distribution:** north-east Atlantic (southern
Biscay to Senegal), Mediterranean, on sandy or rocky ground
in depths of 30-700 m.—**Habits:** a well camouflaged bottom-
living fish which lies in wait for small invertebrates which it
catches with lightning speed as soon as they come near
enough.

Red Gurnard   *Aspitrigla cuculus*

Triglidae

Characteristics: body wedge-shaped with an armoured head, 2 dorsal fins and large pectoral fins in which the lower 3 rays are free and movable, like fingers; these bear sensory organs. Head profile steep, slightly concave, snout with 3 or 4 small spines on each side. Spine above the pectoral fin short, powerful; the pectoral fins extend back to the 3rd anal fin ray. Lateral line with 65-70 tall, bony scales (in contrast to the streaked Gurnard, *Trigloporus lastoviza,* in which there are thin oblique transverse stripes on the flanks). Back and sides reddish, belly whitish, pectoral fins grey, pink or yellowish, anal fin with a pale base and a dark rear edge. average length 20-30 cm, maximum up to 45 cm.—**Distribution:** north-east Atlantic (Scotland, occasionally Norway, to north-west Africa, Mediterranean), in coastal waters (5-250 m).—**Habits:** gurnards can produce low croaking sounds by the action of muscles which set the swimbladder vibrating. Adults feed mainly on crustaceans and small fishes. They spawn in spring and summer, and the eggs and larvae float.

Tub Gurnard   *Trigla lucerna*

Triglidae

Characteristics: body wedge-shaped, with an armoured head, 2 dorsal fins and large pectoral fins with the lower 3 rays free and movable. Snout pointed, with 2 short bony plates. Spine above the pectoral fin short. Body without transverse stripes. Lateral line clearly visible, smooth. Coloration varies according to the environment. Back red, yellowish or brown, sides reddish or yellowish, belly whitish or pink. Pectoral fins red with a pale blue border, and blue spots. Average length 25-50 cm, maximum c. 75 cm.—**Distribution:** north-east Atlantic (Norway to Senegal), Mediterranean, Black Sea, on mud, sand and gravel bottoms in depths of 5-300 m; young fish are frequently found near the coast, in or near estuaries, and even in fresh water.—**Habits:** a bottom-living fish, feeding on crustaceans and fishes. Spawns in winter (Mediterranean) or early summer (English Channel). The eggs and larvae float in the water.

Pogge *Agonus cataphractus*
Agonidae

Characteristics: body completely enclosed in keeled bony plates, head flat and triangular. Two dorsal fins, the 1st with 5-6 spiny rays. Coloration brown, with 4-5 saddle-like markings on the back, belly whitish. Pectoral fins sometimes orange. Anal, ventral and 2nd dorsal fins much larger in male than in female. Average length 12-15 cm, maximum c. 20 cm.—**Distribution:** White and Barents Seas, Norway to North Sea and English Channel, on mud, sand and gravel down to c. 270 m.—**Habits:** usually buried in the bottom or hidden among stones.—**Diet:** invertebrates. Spawning occurs in February-April, the eggs (diameter 1.8-2.2 mm) being laid in clumps, often among the holdfasts of brown seaweeds. After a period of some months they hatch as larvae 6-8 mm long which live in the plankton until they are c. 20 mm long.

Father Lasher *Myoxocephalus scorpius*
Cottidae

Characteristics: body stocky with a broad, flat head, with bony ridges on the skull. Pre-operculum with 2 spines. Skin smooth, scaleless. Two dorsal fins, the 1st with 7-11 spiny rays, anal fin without spiny rays, pectoral fins fan-like. Ventral fins each with 3 fin rays. Coloration usually grey or brownish, with dark spots on the head and back, sides with pale spots, belly yellowish in the male, orange in the female. Fins pale, with dark bands and dots. Maximum length (in arctic waters) c. 60 cm.—**Distribution:** north-east Atlantic (White and Barents Seas to Biscay), Spitsbergen, Iceland, North Sea, on sand, mud and gravel down to 250 m, occasionally in estuaries.—**Habits:** a bottom-living fish, feeding mainly on crustaceans, fish spawn and larvae, and breeding in the winter. When pairing the male grasps the female with his large, rough pectoral fins. The eggs (diameter 2-2.5 mm) are laid in clumps among stones and seaweed and are guarded by the male. They hatch in c. 5 weeks and the larvae remain in the plankton until 15 mm long. They are sexually mature at the end of the 2nd year.

Lumpsucker   *Cyclopterus lumpus*
Cyclopteridae

Characteristics: body thick-set, roundish, scaleless, but with numerous small bony denticles and 4 rows of larger bony plates. Ventral fins fused to form an adhesive disc. Juveniles with 2 dorsal fins, but in adults the 1st dorsal is covered by thick skin. Females have a taller dorsal crest than males and smaller pectoral fins. Coloration brownish, bluish or grey, males at spawning time with an orange or brick-red belly. Males up to 35 cm, females usually to 50 cm, rarely to 60 cm (6-7 kg).—**Distribution:** both sides of Atlantic, in the east southwards to Portugal, in depths of 50-150 m.—**Habits:** a bottom-living fish on rocky ground, where it can attach itself by the suction disc.—**Diet:** invertebrates and small fishes (e.g. gobies). Spawning occurs in February-May, when the female lays a clump of c. 200,000 eggs which are at first yellowish-red, later greenish. These are guarded by the male and they hatch in 1-2 months.

Flying Gurnard   *Dactylopterus volitans*
Cephalacanthidae

Characteristics: body elongated, gurnard-like, with rough scales. Head large, covered with bony plates. Snout short, sloping steeply. Mouth small, semicircular; jaws with small teeth. Eyes large. Pre-operculum with a long spine, gill opening small. Two dorsal fins, the 1st with 2 long spiny rays at the front. Pectoral fins short, with 6 rays anteriorly, only connected at the base to the wing-like rear part. Two keeled scales on either side of the caudal peduncle. Head, back and sides grey or brownish, usually with dark and pale markings, belly reddish-white. Pectoral fins brown, with a regular pattern of pale blue dots and stripes. Maximum length up to 50 cm.—**Distribution:** tropical and subtropical Atlantic coasts (Portugal to Angola, Massachusetts to Argentina, rarely north to Britain), Mediterranean, over sandy and muddy ground, usually in 10-80 m.—**Habits:** similar to those of the gurnards.—**Diet:** mainly small crustaceans. Spawning takes place in summer.

Turbot   *Scophthalmus maximus*   Scophthalmidae

Characteristics: body almost circular, scaleless on the eyed side, but with large, irregularly distributed bony tubercles. Eyes on the left side. Mouth large, the lower jaw protruding. Dorsal and anal fins not reaching the caudal fin. Eyed side grey-brown to dark chocolate-brown, with yellowish, pale or dark brown, blackish or greenish dots. Blind side whitish. Usually up to 80 cm, maximum 100 cm (c. 12 kg); males smaller than females.—**Distribution:** north-east Atlantic (Arctic Circle to Morocco), Mediterranean, over sand, mud and gravel from shallow water down to c. 80 m.—**Habits:** feeds on crustaceans, bivalves and small bottom-living fishes. In northern Europe spawning occurs in April-August, over gravelly ground in depths of 10-80 m. The female lays 10-15 million eggs (each with a large oil globule), and these and the transparent, still symmetrical larvae drift in the plankton. After 4-6 months when 2.5 cm long the young start to live on the bottom in shallow coastal waters. They gradually move into deeper water as they grow. Sexually mature in their 5th year.

Dab   *Limanda limanda*   Pleuronectidae

Characteristics: body oval with a terminal mouth and the eyes on the right side. Head quarter the length of the body. Pre-operculum with a free edge. Lateral line with a semicircular curve over the pectoral fins. Scales on the eyed side rough. Eyed side yellowish-brown, often with indistinct spots and small dark and orange dots, pectoral fins orange. Blind side whitish. Average length c. 20 cm, maximum up to 40 cm.—**Distribution:** north-east Atlantic (White Sea and Iceland to Biscay), North and western Baltic Seas, usually over sandy ground, from shallow water down to depths of c. 200 m.—**Habits:** a common flatfish in the North Sea.—**Diet:** bottom-living animals, including fishes. Spawning occurs in January-August, when the female lays 50,000-150,000 free-floating eggs (diameter 0.7-1 mm) which hatch in 7-14 days into larvae c. 2.5 mm long. At a length of c. 14 cm these acquire the flatfish shape and start to live on the bottom. In the North Sea they are sexually mature in their 2nd or 3rd year (15-20 cm).

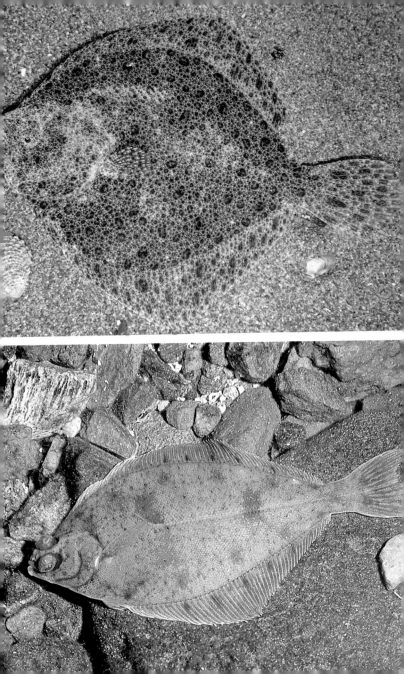

Flounder   *Platichthys flesus*   Pleuronectidae

Characteristics: body oval, and usually with the eyes on the right side. Mouth small. Scales small, smooth, but there are a few coarse, toothed scales at the front of the lateral line and at the base of the dorsal and anal fins. Hybridization with Plaice is not uncommon. The eyed side is greenish or brownish, occasionally with dark and pale orange spots. Blind side whitish. Usually up to 30 cm, maximum up to 50 cm.—**Distribution:** north-east Atlantic and parts of the Mediterranean, from the tidal zone to depths of c. 50 m, in summer also in brackish water and far upstream in rivers.—**Habits:** active at night, remaining buried in sand during the day.—**Diet:** small invertebrates and fishes. Spawning takes place in February-May at depths of 20-40 m in the North sea. The female lays 400,000-2,000,000 free-floating eggs (diameter 0.8-1.4 mm) which hatch in 5-7 days (at c. 10°C) into larvae 3 mm long. At a length of 7-10 mm the young fish start to live on the bottom. Males are sexually mature in their 3rd, females in their 4th year (20-35 cm).

Plaice   *Pleuronectes platessa*   Pleuronectidae

Characteristics: body oval, mouth terminal, pre-operculum with a free edge, scales small, smooth. A series of 4-7 bony knobs runs from the eyes to the start of the lateral line, but there are no prickles at the dorsal and anal fin bases. Eyed side with reddish or orange-yellow spots which have a pale border in older individuals. Average length 25-40 cm, maximum up to 90 cm (7 kg, c. 50 years old).—**Distribution:** north-east Atlantic (White Sea to Portugal) from the tidal zone down to c. 200 m. Also in Mediterranean and Black Seas.—**Habits:** juveniles feed on small worms and crustaceans, adults on large bristle-worms, thin-shelled bivalves and crabs. In the North Sea spawning takes place in depths of 20-40 m at c. 6°C, on well-defined spawning grounds. The 50,000-520,000 eggs (diameter 1.6 mm; without oil globule) drift in the plankton and hatch after 10-20 days into larvae 6 mm long. After 1-2 months, at a length of 12-14 mm, the young fish start to live on the bottom in shallow water. They are usually sexually mature in their 4th or 5th year (males at 20-30 cm, females at 30-40 cm).

134

Common Sole *Solea vulgaris*
Soleidae

Characteristics: body oval with a rounded, scaled head, and eyes on the right side. Mouth ventral, small, curved. Nostrils of the blind side small, widely separated from one another. Eyed side usually brown or grey-brown with large irregular dark spots, the pectoral fin with a black tip. Blind side whitish, its pectoral fin somewhat smaller than that on the eyed side. Average length 30-40 cm, maximum up to c. 60 cm (3 kg; over 20 years old).—**Distribution:** north-east Atlantic (Trondheim to Senegal), North Sea and Mediterranean, on muddy and sandy ground, usually in depths of 10-60 m, moving into deeper, offshore waters (70-130 m) in winter. Also enters estuaries.—**Habits:** active at night and in twilight.—**Diet:** small bottom-living invertebrates and fishes. Spawning occurs in March-April (coasts of Ireland and southern England) or April-July (North Sea), in shallow waters at 6-12°C. The 100,000-150,000 eggs (diameter 1.3-1.5 mm) float in the water and hatch in c. 10 days (at 9-10°C). The larvae remain in the plankton until they acquire the characteristic flatfish shape at a length of 12-15 mm, when they move to the bottom. They are sexually mature in their 3rd-5th year (25-30 cm).

Monochirus hispidus
Soleidae

Characteristics: body oval with a rounded, scaled head with eyes on the right side. Mouth small, terminal and curved. Scales large, pointed, "hairy". No pectoral fin on the blind side. Eyed side usually grey or yellowish-brown, with dark marbling which extends on to the dorsal and anal fins as rows of regular spots. Caudal peduncle with a V-shaped marking. Maximum length up to 14 cm.—**Distribution:** east Atlantic coasts (Portugal to Ghana), Mediterranean, on muddy and sandy ground in depths of 10-250 m.—**Habits:** spends the day buried in sand with only the eyes showing and starts to become active at twilight.—**Diet:** small bottom-living invertebrates. Spawning takes place in late summer. Swims with powerful strokes of tail just above the bottom, and always with the eyed side upwards.

Microchirus ocellatus
Soleidae

Characteristics: body longish-oval with a rounded, scaled head and eyes on the right side. Mouth small, ventral and curved. Lateral line with 70-75 scales. Dorsal and anal fins not joined to the caudal fin. Pectoral fin on the blind side small, with fewer rays than that on the eyed side. Coloration usually greyish-yellow, pale or chocolate-brown with large dark markings on the front of the body. Adults with several large black spots with pale edges. Caudal peduncle with dark stripes, rear edge of caudal fin with a narrow white border. Maximum length up to 20 cm.—**Distribution:** north-east Atlantic (Portugal to Mauritania, Madeira, Canaries), Mediterranean, on muddy and sandy ground from shallow water down to 300 m.—**Habits:** little appears to be known about the life history of this species which is only rarely found.

Sunfish *Mola mola*
Molidae

Characteristics: body disc-shaped and much laterally compressed, without a caudal peduncle and with a thick, scaleless, leathery skin. Mouth small, each jaw with one beak-like tooth. Gill openings close in front of the pectoral fins. Dorsal and anal fins tall, lobe-like, caudal fin in the form of a stiff skin fold joined to the dorsal and anal. Ventral fins lacking. Back and the dorsal and anal fins grey, brownish or greenish, sides and belly paler. Maximum length c. 3 m (1,400 kg).—**Distribution:** widespread in all temperate and tropical seas (except South Pacific), in the north-east Atlantic from Scandinavia and Iceland to Madeira and Azores; also in Mediterranean.—**Habits:** lives in the open sea, occasionally coming up to the surface; it has been suggested that this may be due to age or sickness.—**Diet:** crustaceans, echinoderms, squid, fishes and algae. The female lays over 300 million eggs. The larvae, which have long spines and normal fins, drift in the plankton.

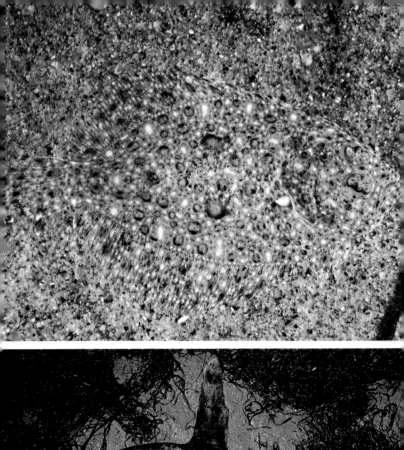
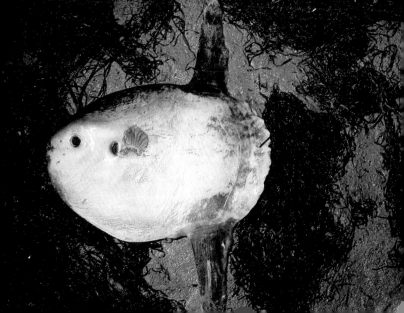

Cornish Sucker   *Lepadogaster lepadogaster*

Gobiesocidae

Characteristics: body slender, laterally compressed, with a flat, triangular head. Skin scaleless, slimy. Head profile sloping fairly steeply, eyes large, very mobile. Mouth wide, jaws long and beak-like, the upper jaw protruding. Lips fleshy, the front nostril with a large fleshy flap. Dorsal and anal fins positioned far back, without spiny rays, and joined to the caudal fin. Ventral fins modified to form a suction disc. Two pale blue eye spots with a dark brown, red or black border on the back behind the eyes. Maximum length up to 8 cm.—**Distribution:** north-east Atlantic (Shetlands to Senegal), Mediterranean, on rocky shores with algal growths. —**Habits:** often seen in tidal pools, clinging to rocks. Spawning occurs in spring and summer. The clumps of golden eggs adhere to rocks and are guarded by one of the parents.

Angler   *Lophius piscatorius*

Lophiidae

Characteristics: body broad, flat with soft, scaleless skin, a broad head and a wide, semi-circular mouth. Lower jaw protruding, teeth large and curved. Gill openings as small slits close behind the pectoral fins. First dorsal fin ray free-standing, elongated, with a lobe-like skin flap (the "angle"), 2nd and 3rd rays also free-standing. Pectoral fins enlarged to form arm-like structures, ventral fins small, on the underside of the head. Back brownish, greenish-brown or reddish with dark markings. Belly white. Average length 40-60 cm, maximum up to 198 cm (30-40 kg).—**Distribution:** both sides of the Atlantic, on sandy and muddy ground from the coasts down to 500-600 m. In the north-east Atlantic from Barents Sea to Guinea.—**Habits:** a predator feeding on small fishes and bottom-living invertebrates. Spawning occurs in late winter and spring, the female laying c. 1 million eggs embedded in broad, violet gelatinous bands (length 8-10 m, breadth 15-45 cm) which are torn apart by wave action and the pieces then float in the water. The young move down to the bottom when 5-8 cm long.

INDEX   English Names

Latin Names